D1231686

THE QUACKS OF OLD LONDON

THE QUACKS OF
OLD LONDON

By

C. J. S. THOMPSON

BARNES
&NOBLE
BOOKS
NEW YORK

This edition published by Barnes & Noble, Inc.

1993 Barnes & Noble Books

ISBN 1-56619-154-8

Printed and bound in the United States of America

M 9 8 7 6 5 4 3 2 1

FOREWORD

ALTHOUGH quackery has existed in one form or another from time immemorial, little is known of the quack-doctors who began to flourish in England about the sixteenth century. Medicine in particular, appears ever to have attracted pretenders and it is the art in which they have been most successful. There have always been unfortunate sufferers in despair, ready to become the dupes of the charlatans, and so in the seventeenth century, we find the ranks of the quacks were increased by a host of boasting rogues and cunning rascals, who flocked to London and soon became prominent in the social life of the time.

The following century was the golden age of the quacks and they were patronised by all classes, from the King to the peasant. Advertising was the mainspring of their success, and the bills by means of which they made their nostrums known, throw a considerable light on the manner in which they preyed on the credulity of the public.

Many of these quaintly-worded effusions, with their rhymes and curious illustrations, which have now been brought together from various collections, are of great rarity and are published for the first time.

CONTENTS

CONTENTS

CHAPTER III

CHAPTER IV

CHAPTER V

CONTENTS

CHAPTER VI

CHAPTER VII

CHAPTER VIII

CONTENTS

CONTENTS

CHAPTER XI

CHAPTER XII

CHAPTER XIII

CONTENTS

CONTENTS

CHAPTER XVI

CHAPTER XVII

CONTENTS

CHAPTER XVIII

CHAPTER XIX

CHAPTER XX

CONTENTS

and Hogarth—Ballads in her honour—A song in
"The Husband's Relief"—Her Plate at Epsom—
Her end in the Seven Dials—Three great quacks—
"An epistle to a young student at Cambridge"—
Foote's satire on a quack's bill—Skit on a quack's
harangue—Evolution of a quack.

CHAPTER XXI

Colonel Dalmahoy and his wonderful wig—A ballad
on the Colonel—The famous Dr. Rock—Dr. Bossy of
Covent Garden—His talk with the parrot—Richard-
son's parrot intervenes—A story of the famous bird—
Dr. Mantacinni—How he brought the dead to life—
His celebrated "Baume de Vie"—Katterfelto and
his black cats—His exhibition in Piccadilly—His
Solar microscope—His artful advertisements.

CHAPTER XXII

Martin van Butchell and his white pony with purple
spots—His dental practise—His wife's body embalmed—"The dear departed" kept in his sitting
room—An Epitaph on the lady—The second wife
objects—John Hill, botanist, playwright and quack-
doctor—Garrick's lines on his plays—"The Inspector"—A ballad on his death.

CHAPTER XXIII

Physicians and quack remedies—Dr. Brodum and his
"Nervous Cordial"—He is hailed before the College
of Physicians—How he got his diploma—Dr. Solo-
mon and his "Cordial Balm of Gilead"—His "Balm
of Gold" and its composition—Lady patient's fond-
ness for the remedy—The irate husband's revenge—
The quack's punishment—James Graham and his
Temple of Health—The Grand Celestial Bed—The
Magnetic Throne—Temple of Health and Hymen in
Pall Mall—His religious mania.

CONTENTS
CHAPTER XXIV

THE QUACKS OF OLD LONDON

INTRODUCTION

QUACKERY goes back to the beginning of human history and has existed in all ages down to the present day. From the records of the early civilisations, there is evidence of its practise over four thousand years ago, and it may therefore be said to form an integral part of humanity.

Its growth was fostered by the early association of the healing art with priest-craft, for human credulity, especially in connexion with sickness, has altered but little throughout the centuries, and there have always been individuals ready to prey on the foibles and weaknesses of their fellows.

The control of mysterious and unknown powers, has ever been a quality which persons of ordinary ability could not successfully acquire, so there arose a class of specialists ; men, who by their superior knowledge and cleverness, made others believe that they were able to cope with the unseen. These, in ancient times, were the priest-magicians who may fitly be called the first quack-doctors. They practised a mystical form of quackery that had its origin in charms and incantations, which they employed not only to cure but also to prevent disease.

This was followed by belief in the healing virtue of water, springs, relics and shrines and thus, after beginning in simple faith, this form of mysticism developed into deliberate trickery which was eventually exploited for personal gain.

The early Babylonian priest-physician sometimes sprinkled water over a sick person while he repeated an incantation, or words of power, with the object of expelling the evil spirit that was believed to be the cause of the disease. A clay tablet, in cunieform, dating from about 2500 years B.C., thus records the words used :

"When I sprinkle the water of Ea on the sick man,
    When I subdue the sick man."

In another it is directed to "wash him with the purest water," in order to effect the cure.

In ancient Egypt the priest-physicians were the chief practitioners of the healing art which they enveloped in mystery, their secrets being jealously guarded and hidden from the laity. The belief in charms and amulets was universal, and quackery was doubtless rampant.

There were quack doctors also among the early peoples of India, and Charaka, one of the traditional Hindu physicians, alludes contemptuously to " those who making a great display in the train of a learned doctor, who no sooner did they hear of a patient, than they hurried off to him to fill his ears with their own medical ability."

In ancient Greece, the rhizotomists or root-cutters who sold secret remedies, love philtres and cosmetics to the credulous, were well versed in quackery ; while

in Rome in the time of the Empire, there were quack
doctors innumerable.

To them we probably owe the introduction of quackery
into Britain at the time of the Roman occupation, for a
"medicine stamp" discovered at Bath some years ago,
shows that a quack called Junianus, sold a " Golden
Ointment to clear the sight," to the citizens of the
ancient city on the Avon.

Among the Arabs who cultivated pharmacy and had a
considerable knowledge of the use of drugs, the quack
doctor was known as early as the tenth century.
Rhazes the famous Arabian physician who was the first
accurately to describe smallpox and measles, referring
to the charlatans of his time, says : " There are so many
little arts used by mountebanks and pretenders to
physic, that an entire treatise would not contain them.
Their impudence is equal to their guilt in tormenting
persons in their last hours. They profess to cure the
falling sickness (epilepsy) by making an issue at the
back of the head in the form of a cross. Others give
out they can draw snakes out of their patient's noses,
or worms from their teeth. No wise man ought to trust
his life to their hands."

During the Middle Ages, there was no line between
the regular practitioner of medicine and the pretender
to the art of healing.

Henri de Mondeville, who was surgeon to Philip the
Fair, writing between 1306 and 1320 in his treatise on
"Chirurgie," alludes to the "unlearned persons, barbers,
fortune-tellers, old women, who give themselves out for
surgeons in order to gain a living." He says that " Kings,

Princes and Prelates, Canons, Curates, Religios, Dukes, Noblemen and Burgesses, dabble without knowledge in dangerous surgical treatments and especially in the treatment of diseases of the eye, which is dangerous, difficult and fraudulent to that degree, that one seldom finds a surgeon who is capable and expert in those matters. The vulgar say of these religious and their like, that they have knowledge infused into them by the pure grace of the Creator." Here again we have the association of religion and medicine which has survived to modern times.

CHAPTER I

QUACKERY may of course be practised in various ways and in connexion with various callings, so it will be well, before describing the activities of the quack-doctor of medicine, to consider the meanings ascribed to the word.

The quack-doctor in early literature is alluded to as a mountebank, an empiric, and a charlatan. The "Oxford Dictionary" defines the quack as "an ignorant pretender to medical and surgical skill, who boasts to have a knowledge of wonderful remedies, an empiric, an impostor in medicine." Skeat in his " Etymological Dictionary of the English Language " gives the meaning of quack, " to cry up pretended nostrums " and observes it is only a particular use of the original word " to make a noise like a duck." He further says, "Quack-salver is a derivative which means a quack who puffs up his salves or ointments and later was quack-doctor. The word originally meant a mountebank who sold salves and eye lotions at country fairs."

Quack-salver is said by some authorities to be derived from the old Dutch word *Kwabzalver* from *kwab* a wen, and *zalver* an ointment, while others assert the name originated from *Quecksilber* the German for quicksilver. The earliest allusion to it in English literature is made by Gosson, in " Schoole of Abuse " printed in 1579, who mentions, "A quacke-saluer's Budget of filthy receites." In the seventeenth century the word is frequently used, as in Ben Jonson's "Volpone," 1605, "they are quack-saluers, fellowes that live by senting oyles and drugs ", while in 1608, Dekker alludes to " Quack-saluing Empiricks."

The word mountebank is mentioned by Stanyhurst in his "Description of Ireland" as early as 1577, and applies to " the travelling quack who from a platform appealed to his audience by means of stories, tricks and jugglings, often assisted by a clown or fool."

The word charlatan came into use in the early seventeenth century and Ben Jonson in " Volpone " alludes to " the rabble of these ground Ciarlitani that spread their clokes on the pavement." Sir Thomas Browne also mentions " Saltimbancoes, Quack-salvers and Charlatans " in " Pseudoxia Epidemica " in 1646. Randle Cotgrave defines the word as meaning "a mountebanke, a cousening drug-seller, a prattling quack-salver."

An empiric was not necessarily a quack, and although the word was often used in that sense in the sixteenth and seventeenth centuries, it became later to be more properly applied to an experimenter who gained his education or knowledge of his art by hearsay and observation. He who practised by rule of thumb without rational grounds.

The quack-doctor was recognised in London as early as 1382, for according to Stow, a " counterfeit physician " in that year "was set on horseback, his face to the horse's tail, the same tail in his hand as a bridle, a collar of Jordans about his neck, a whetstone on his breast and so led through the City of London with ringing of basons, and then banished." There is record of another counterfeit physician who lost his head, which was exposed on the Tower in 1426. Such were the punishments for quacks in London in the fourteenth and fifteenth centuries.

It was not until the time of Henry VIII in 1511, that an Act was passed for the regulation of medical and surgical practise with powers to suppress quack practitioners. The opening sentences of this statute are interesting, as they give us some idea of the extent to which quackery was practised at that period.

" Forasmuch as the science and cunning of physick and surgery, is daily within this realm, exercised by a great multitude of ignorant persons, of whom the greater part have no manner of insight in the same, nor any other kind of learning ; that common artificers as smiths, weavers and women, boldly and accustomably take upon them great cures and things of great difficulty in which they partly use sorcery and witchcraft, partly apply such medicines unto the disease as to be noxious and nothing meet, therefore to the High displeasure of God, great infamy to the Faculty, and the grievous hurt and damage and destruction of many of the King's liege people."

When the College of Physicians was founded seven years later, it was granted a charter conferring upon it

larger powers for the suppression of quacks and impostors, but in spite of this, they continued to increase
and flourish, and in Tudor times, " Ministers, Mountebanks, Runnagate Quack-salvers and women ", says a
writer of the time, infested old London.

Thomas Gale, who was a surgeon in the Army in 1544
tells us that in that year, " I did see in the two hospitals
of London called St. Thomas's and St. Bartholomews,
to the number of 300 and odd poor people that were
diseased of sore arms, legs, feet and hands with other
parts of the body, so grievously infected, that 120 of
them could never be recovered without loss of a limb.
All these were brought to their mischief by witches, by
women, and by counterfeit Javils (worthless fellows)
that take upon them the use of art, not only robbing
them of their money but of their limbs and perpetual
health."

John Halle, a worthy doctor of Maidstone, describes
the " javells who thronged to that town from London
in 1565."

He says, one Thomas Lufkin, a fuller by trade, came
there in 1558 and announced, " If any man, woman or
child be sick or would be let blood or be diseased with
any manner of inward or outward griefs, as all manner
of agues or fevers, pleurisies, colic, stone, strangulation,
imposthumes, pustules, kanker, gout, bone-ache and
pain of the joints which cometh for lack of blood letting,
let them resort to the ' Saracen's Head ' in the East
Lane and they shall have remedy by me, Thomas
Lufkin."   Another quack was John Bewley who
hailed from the Old Bailey, and lived opposite Sir

Robert Charnley. Bewley was arrested at Maidstone and brought before the justices who found he could not read.   He was let off with a caution, and advised "to leave such false and naughty deceits and begone," and promptly returned to the scene of his former activities in London.

The quack has always shown great skill in advertising and recognised it as the mainspring of success. Before the era of printing he had to rely solely on his lungs for haranguing his audience, but in the sixteenth century he began to appreciate the value of the press in making known his remedies and commenced to circulate hand-bills.

A fragment of one of these bills printed about 1525, is preserved in the library of the Royal College of Surgeons. It reads as follows :

"The Canker or the Colyck and the Skarre in the lyppe or other diseases in the mouth . . .

Also, if any man hade any dysease in his eyen who be with Spurblindness or a Wem or any other Skynne over the Syghts. These and other such lyke diseases can this aforesaid MAYSTER AVOYDE AND HEALE by the grace and helpe of God. Moreover yf any be diseased with the pockes or other pryby diseases or have sore legges of old or

newe greves, let him come to the forsayde
MAISTER GERNAES which is
lodged in Saint Thomas hospital long
Southwarck and he wyl heale him with
the grace of God; the poore freely for the
honor and love of God and the ryche for
a reasonable rewarde."

GOD SAVE THE KING."

About the middle of the sixteenth century, the College
of Physicians on being urged to take more active steps
to check the practise of the quacks, began to take proceedings against some of the more flagrant offenders,
and summoned them to appear before the President and
Censors, who had power to commit them to prison.

The account of these proceedings recorded by Charles
Goodall, throws a further light on the quacks of the
period. From him we learn that in 1551, a man
named Grig, who was a poulterer in Surrey, posed as a
prophet and healer, and said he was able to cure divers
diseases. His activities were cut short by the officials
of the College, and on the 8th of September of that year
he was put in the pillory at Southwark to expiate his
offence.

In 1555, during the reign of Queen Mary, one Charles
Cornet, "an impudent and ignorant Buffoon, who
would not be restrained from his ill practises, with the
bills of his condemnation affixed at the corners of
streets, being patronised by Weston, Dean of Westminster and Robert Charnley, was forced to flee the

town and had his unwholesome remedies burnt in the open market at Westminster."

In the time of Queen Elizabeth, many of the quacks practising in London were Italians, and in 1570, one of these called Sylva was brought before the President and Censors of the College. He was charged with having undertaken to cure an old woman by suffumigations with which she died and "presented Stibium (antimony) to another person to his great prejudice." He was fined Twenty pounds and afterwards committed to prison. On October 28th 1586, Peter Piers was hailed before the College tribunal and sent to prison "for giving Pills of Antimony, Turbith (sulphate of mercury) and Mercury sublimate, by which he killed several persons."

Paul Fairfax, another quack who gave out bills "stuffed with arrogance and ostentation of the Admirable Virtues of a Water which he called Aqua Coelestis, with which he cheated people, when brought before the College, confessed that he had practised physick in London for four months." He pretended that he had done several cures with his water and other remedies, but without avail, for he was fined five pounds and warned, that if he continued his evil doings, he would be sent to prison.

The female quack was not unknown in the sixteenth century, for in 1588, we find that Tomazine Scarlet, " a woman so egregiously ignorant that she confessed she knew nothing of Physick, neither could read or write, yet had hundreds under her cure to whom she gave medicines, Stibium, etc., was charged with these base practises. She was fined Ten pounds and was committed to prison for her mis-deeds."

Paul Buck, who is said to have been " a very impudent and ignorant quack," who had been practising in London for six years, pretending to cure all diseases ; apparently gave a great deal of trouble. He was committed to prison in 1589 until he could give bond with security, " upon which he refused to give any bond and said he would practise when he liked." He was evidently a contumacious rogue and on giving this " insolent and sawcy answer," he was remanded back to the Counter (prison) in Wood Street. Buck however was not without influential friends, for he got Sir Frances Walsingham, Secretary to Her Majesty, to write to the President of the College stating, " that he had done much good and was otherwise of a verie good and honest disposition." On receipt of this letter, the Beadle of the College was sent to bring Buck before the President again, but he refused to come.

Meanwhile, he was ingratiating himself with the Keeper of the prison, for about two months afterwards, he appears to have been set at liberty without the knowledge of the College. Once free, he recommenced practise but was soon pounced upon and again brought before the tribunal. This time, he procured letters from Lord Howard, the Lord High Admiral, praying the College to grant him a licence to practise and offering twenty pounds (May 29. 1593) for the same, but this was refused. Even then Buck was not at the end of his resources, for he produced a letter from the Earl of Essex commending him, but this did not move the authorities, who refused the licence and again fined him.

Another notorious mountebank and impostor was Roger Powel, who was cited to appear before the College, " for that he had hanged up a table in several parts of the town wherein he boasted of his great cures and long experience." Although he produced letters from the Queen giving an account of his poverty and fortunate success in physick, he was fined twenty pounds and sent to the Counter. Out of respect to the Earl of Derby, with whom he claimed relationship, he was released from prison upon giving bond that he would never practise in London or within seven miles of the city.

The notorious Simon Forman, who claimed to be an alchemist and astrologer and a practitioner of magic, was brought before the College and charged with pretending to cure " many Hectical and tabid people by the use of an Electuary made with rose juice and wormwood water. He confessed that he had practised physick for sixteen years and for two years in London. He was mulcted in Five pounds but did not pay it, so was brought back after two or three years and committed to prison, but he was released soon after by order of the Lord Keeper. He fled to Lambeth as a place of protection from the College officers, but continued to practise astrology and fortune-telling."

Towards the close of the sixteenth century an Englishman named Francis Anthony, who had taken the degree of master of arts at Cambridge, proceeded to Hamburg to study medicine. After obtaining his diploma, he returned to London and commenced to practise as a

doctor of physic but without a licence from the College
of Physicians. In consequence, he was hailed before the
President and Censors, and on examination, he confessed that he had "practised physick in London for
six months and during that period had cured twenty or
more divers diseases in people to whom he had given
purging and vomiting physick. To others he had given
a disphoretick medicine prepared from gold and mercury." He was questioned in several parts of physick
by the Censors and found very weak and ignorant, whereupon he was fined Twenty pounds and committed to
the Counter prison. He was liberated in 1602, but a
few years afterwards fresh charges were laid against
him "by a Reverend Divine, who upon his deathbed,
complained that a medicine called Aurum Potabile
given to him by Anthony had killed him."

This caused him to publish a defence of his remedy in
which he revealed the recipe, although he still kept
secret the process for making it.

There was a popular belief in the sixteenth century,
that gold possessed great and remarkable medicinal
properties, and it was actually said to contain the principles of immortality. A solution of the precious metal,
therefore, was highly valued.

Anthony's recipe for his preparation is particularly
interesting, as it shows he had some knowledge of
chemistry.

His process was published in the form of a little
pamphlet which was printed in London by William
Cooper in 1683, although he made known his recipe in
1610. It is called "Receit showing the way to make his

most Excellent Medicine called AURUM POTABILE," and the following is a brief summary of the process.

A piece of block tin was first to be placed in any iron pan and heated continuously until it became like ashes. Four ounces of these ashes were then to be placed in a flask with three pints of strong red wine and digested for two or three days. The clear liquid was to be distilled and four ounces of fresh tin ashes added to it and a quart of red wine. This was to be digested for ten days, filtered, distilled and a pint of vinegar added to the residue which was to be heated for ten days and then again distilled. This distillate he called the menstruum.

"Then," he states, "take one ounce of pure refined Gold which costs £3 13s. 4d., and file it into dust, heat it with an equal quantity of white salt and subject it to heat for four hours. Grind this very small and after calcining it, wash it with boiling water repeatedly. One ounce of the residue is to be then digested with half a pint of the menstruum and heated for six days. After again being distilled, the residuum dried and powdered, is to be put into half a pint of spirit of wine, left for ten days and then poured off." This operation is to be repeated three times and the liquors then distilled until they are the thickness of a syrup. One ounce of this is to be put into a pint of canary sack and the solution is ready for use."

Divested of all the unnecessary operations which formed part of the mysteries of the alchemist, who loved to create an atmosphere of great labour, Anthony doubtless got a solution of stannate of gold. The sale of the remedy was so successful, that it was carried on by his son for some time after his death.

The practise of quackery in London at the end of the sixteenth century is thus graphically described by a contemporary writer and quoted in his own words : " The whol Rable of these quack-Saluers are of a base wit and perverse. They for the most part are the abject and sordidous scumme and refuse of the people, who having run away from their trades and occupations learne in a corner to get their livings by killing men, and if we plucke off their vizards wherein these maskers do march and bring them to the light, which like owls they cannot abide, they will appear to be runnagate Jews, the Cut-throats and robbers of christians, slow-bellyed monkes who have made their escape from their cloysters, simoniacall and perjured shavelings, shifting and outcast Pettifoggers, Trasonical Chymists, light-headed and trivial Druggers and Apothecaries, sun-shunning nightbirds and corner-creepers, dull-pated and base Mechanickes, Stage players, Juglers, Pedlers, Prittle-pratling barbers, filthie Grasiers, curious bath keepers, common shifters, cogging cavaliers, lazy clowns, toothless and tatling old wives, chattering char-women, long-tongued mid-wives, Dog-leeches and such like baggage.

" In the next ranke follow the Poysoners, Inchanters, Soothsayers, Wizards, Fortune-tellers, Magitians, Witches, Hags, with a rablement of that damnable crew. For the greatest part of them disdaine booke-learning, being altogether unacquainted with liberal arts and never came where learning grew. Meere dolts, idiots and buzzards.

" You shall sooner finde a blacke swan than an honest man in this Bunch, but you shall discerne notorious Impostors, old beaten foxes and cozeners, having a foxe's head and a whorish and wainscotted face. Hee will make sure to fawne upon the Female kinde and to purchase favour of honourable ladies with some rare pretious gifts, suppose a piece of counterfeit Unicorn's Horn, or a Bezoar Stone made of powder of post or glasse sand, the onely and soveraigne antidote and medicine for all maladies.

" Some under the names and tytles of Elixir of Lyfe, Quin-Essence of Gold, Pearle, Azoth and Panacea, and account Secret of Secrets, do sell certaine Gimmals with great applause.

"Others refer unto Charms, witchcraft, magnisicall incantations and sorcerie, affirming, there is no way to help them but by characters, Circles, Exercisms, Conjurations, and other impious means. Others sell at great price certaine Amulets of Gold and Silver, stamped under selected constellations of the planets and some magicall character, shamelessly boasting that they will cure all diseases."

Thus Oberndorf, in 1602, quaintly describes, no doubt with some accuracy, the kind of people who swelled the ranks of the quacks of London in the time of the Tudors.

CHAPTER II

FAMOUS QUACKS IN THE TIME OF THE STUARTS

DURING the seventeenth century quacks of every description abounded and flourished in London. At this period, the legitimate practise of medicine was more a pursuit of systems, rather than an application of the principles of pathology then known. During this experimental stage, it is not to be wondered, that quacks sprang up ready to undertake what the regular practitioner could not cure.

Thus the folly of mankind, which is ever ready to deceive itself, and the frequent failure of medicine to give speedy relief in human suffering, threw many into the hands of the quacks who did not scruple to boast they were able to cure every disease incident to man. Besides the more prominent and notorious figures who made their nostrums known by bills, there were the astrologers and fortune-tellers, the women doctors, the beauty-specialists, the mountebanks who harangued their dupes from tables or stages, who congregated in the neighbourhood of Tower-hill and Moorfields, and the general rabble of rogues and rascals who were out to deceive any credulous person with whom they could come in contact. Such was their increase in numbers and audacity that in the time of James I, a warrant was sent to all magistrates in the city, " to take up all reputed Empiricks and Quacks with other offenders of this nature, and bring them before the Censors of the College of Physicians, and the King himself sent letters to the Lord Mayor of London, to the same effect." The College was given further power to fine, search, also to correct and govern these persons, and to punish such as unlawfully practised. But although the authorities began to renew their activities they appear to have prosecuted but few offenders.

Among them was Arthur Dee, a mountebank, who was summoned before the Censors, for " hanging out a table at his door, on which he exposed to sale several medicines by which many diseases were said to be certainly cured." This " crime was esteemed such an intolerable cheat and imposture, that he was ordered to appear with his remedies in order to the inflicting a due penalty upon him." The penalty which was no doubt inflicted is not recorded.

In 1627, they hailed before them a more notorious rogue in the person of John Lambe, " a bold quack, who was charged with demanding forty to fifty pounds for his cures as lately of a Mr. Pickering in Cheapside, who died in his hands."

John Lambe, who was undoubtedly a great scoundrel, had an extraordinary career. He began life as a tutor, after which he took up the study of medicine but soon developed a taste for the magical arts, which he found more profitable than healing the sick. He settled at Tardebigg in Worcestershire for a time, where he made a living by telling fortunes and crystal gazing. In 1608 he was brought before the magistrates and charged with practising magic, was found guilty and committed to prison. On regaining his liberty he went to Hindlip, where he again commenced operations as a magician, but he soon got into trouble and a few months afterwards, was arraigned at the assizes on a charge of having "invoked and entertained certain evil and impious spirits." At the trial it was also asserted that, "he had caused apparitions to proceed from a crystal glass." According to the indictment, he was also charged with degrading "the profession of that noble and deepe science of Physicke, which many base Impostours have used to lewde and juggling practices."

Further, "with not having the feare of God before his eyes, but by a Diabolicall instigation, being mooved and seduced the 16th day of December in yeare of the raigne of our Soveraigne, Lord King James of England, France and Ireland, with certaine Evill, Diabolicall and Execrable arts called witchcrafts, enchantments, charmers and sorcerers, in and upon the right Honourable Th. Lo. W. Devilishly, maliciously and feloniously did use, practise and exercise to the intent by the same Evill, Devillish and Execrable arts, to disable, make infirm and consume the body and strength of the said Th. Lo. W."

He was committed a prisoner to Worcester Castle and while there, some strange things are said to have happened. On one occasion, when he was being visited by three of his friends, and wishing to entertain them, he asked the gaoler for four cups. On these being forthcoming, he conjured "a bottle of sack on the table with which they regaled themselves." He boldly declared that evil would befall his judges, and on the assertion that "the High Sheriff and divers other Justices would die within a fortnight after his trial," he was transferred to King's Bench prison in London, where he was kept in durance for fifteen years. While there he seems to have been plentifully supplied with money and lived well.

On regaining his liberty, he again commenced to tell fortunes and to practice crystal-gazing, living a wild and dissolute life on his gains. In 1627, when he was brought before the Censors of, the College, the chief witness against him was a Mr. Evans, "who" states the record, "gave an account against him in these very words. The persons to whom Lambe, that notable mountebank and impostor, gave physick were, Mr. Springman a mercer, Mr. Wilson the Keeper of Newgate ; by shewing him tricks in a crystal he got from Mr. Peny forty shillings. He gave Physick to the Countess of Exeter and by means of delusions in a crystal, insinuates himself into Ladies esteem and conceits. On Saturday last he got fifty pounds for a cure."

In his defence, Lambe produced a letter from the Bishop of Durham stating, that " he hath done many and great cures."

"This Lambe," concludes the record, "was very famous throughout the Town, being admired for his great skill in the hidden Arts of Magick and Astrology, but in truth he was a wretched knave."

He is said to have been frequently consulted and employed as a tool, by George Villiers, Duke of Buckingham, and to have supplied him with love-philtres and other concoctions. Lambe apparently obtained a strong influence over the Duke, and when the latter fell from Royal favour and as his unpopularity grew, it was shared by his " creature," who was commonly known as " the Duke's devil." One night, after attending the play, Lambe was set upon by a mob of apprentices, who were incensed by a charge that had been made against him, and was so beaten and maltreated that he died from the effects shortly afterwards.

THE ATTACK ON DR. LAMBE
From a woodcut 1628

Lambe's fate showed the popular hatred of Buckingham and the common cry of the London mob was,

" Let Charles and George do what they can,
The Duke shall die like Dr. Lambe."

On the day of Lambe's death, bills bearing the following words were posted on the walls of London.

> "Who rules the Kingdom ? —The King,
> Who rules the King ?—The Duke,
> Who rules the Duke ?—The Devil.

"Let the Duke look to it or he will be served as his doctor was served."

A few weeks later, Buckingham was assassinated.

A curious case brought before the Censors of the College in the time of Charles I, was that of Mr. Evans, a Minister, who was charged with having poisoned Sir Nathaniel Kitch and Lady Amye Blunt by his Antimonial Cup, in Charter House Yard.

Cups made of an alloy of antimony and tin called *pocula emetica* were used in the XVIth and XVIIth centuries. They were filled with wine, which when allowed to stand in them for some days, became sufficiently impregnated with tartar emetic to produce vomiting, when swallowed. No further record beyond the statement that " he was sent to prison," is made of this interesting case.

A more genial and witty quack was Thomas Saffold, whose quaint rhymes and doggerel amused the Town in the time of Charles II.

He was born about 1640 and began life as a weaver, but by some means he managed to pick up a smattering of medical knowledge. On September 4th 1674 he obtained a licence to practice medicine from the Bishop of London, an easy matter for any plausible rogue at that time, as the records of these episcopal licences, still to be found in the library of Lambeth Palace, readily testify.

He established himself at " the *Black Ball* and *Old Lilly's Head,* next door to the *Feather Shops* that are within *Black-Friers Gateway,* which is over against *Ludgate Church,* just by Ludgate in London."

He describes himself, as " an Approved and Licensed Physician and Student in Astrology, who (through God's mercy) to do good." Tom Saffold was a firm believer in advertising, and along Cheapside, Fleet Street and the Strand, and thence down to Whitehall and St. James's, he stationed his bill distributors who gave out his poetic effusions to those who passed by.

He believed himself to be a man of great talent which he determined to exploit to the utmost, and so he announced in one of his bills :

> " It hath so pleased God the King of Heaven,
> Being he to him hath Knowledge given,
> And in him there can be no greater Sin,
> Than to hide his Talent in a Napkin.
> His Candle is Light, and he will not under
> A bushel put it ; Let the World wonder,
> Though he be traduced by such like Tools,
> As have knave's hearts, lack brains are Fools."

Saffold practised what he called " Christian astrology," solved mysteries, answered all lawful questions, provided his patients with lodgings if they required them, and " By God's blessing cured the sick of any age or sex of any distemper."

He made no charge for his advice, if his patients bought a bottle of his wonderful Elixir or a box of his famous Pills, as one of his bills proclaims,

" THE SICK MAY HAVE ADVICE FOR NOTHING "
    And good medicines cheap, if so they please,
    For to cure any curable disease.
    It's Saffold's Pills much better than the rest,
    Deservedly have gain'd the name of Best ;
    In curing by the Cause, quite purging out
    Of Scurvy, French-Pox, Agues, Stone and Gout.
    The head, Stomach, Belly and the Reins, they
    Will cleanse and cure, while you may work or play.
    His pills have often, to their Maker's Praise,
    Cur'd in all weathers, yea in the Dog-Days.
    In short no Purging Med'cine is made, can
    Cure more Diseases in Man or Wo-man,
    Than his cheap Pills, but Three shillings the Box,
    A sure Cure for the Running Reins and Pox.
    Each Box contains thirty six Pills, I'm sure
    As good as e're were made, Scurvy to cure.
    The half box, eighteen pills for eighteen pence,
    Though 'tis too cheap in any Man's own sense."

His Liquor or Elixir, which he recommended for the same diseases, he sold at half a crown a bottle and declared it would cure " Dropsie, Agues, Stone and Gout, as well as the Disease too much in fashion." Saffold in his bills particularly warns his patients not to mistake his house, as " another being near him pretends the same." " To those conceited fools and dark animals who ask how he came to be able to work such great cures, and to fore-tell such great things," he thus replies:

" Dear Friends, let your disease be what God will
Pray to him for a Cure, try Saffold's skill ;
Who may be such a healing Instrument,
As will cure you to your Heart's content.
His medicines are Cheap and truly good,
Being full as safe as your daily food.
Saffold, he can do what may be done, by
Either Physick or true Astrology ;
His best Pills, Rare Elixir and Powder,
Do each Day Praise him Lowder and Lowder.
Dear Countrymen, I pray you be so wise,
When men Back-bite him, believe not their Lyes,
But go and see him and believe your own Eyes.
Then he will say, you are honest and kind,
Try before you judge and Speak as you find."

Tom, as he was popularly called, was continually turning out new rhymes and fresh bills, and one of the last he issued in the form of a ballad runs as follows :

" Some Envious Men being grieved may say,
What need bills thus still be given away ?
Answer. New People come to London every day.
Believing Solomon's advice is right,
I will do what I do with all my might.
Also unless an English Proverb lies,
Practice brings experience and makes wise ;
Experimental knowledge I protest
In Lawful Arts and Science is the best,
Instead of Finis, Saffold ends with Rest."

Another of Saffold's rhymes ran :

" Saffold Resolves, as in his bills exprest
When asked in good earnest, not in Jest ;
He can cure when God Almighty pleases,
But cannot protect against Diseases.

If men will live intemperate and Sin,
He cannot help't if they be sick agen.
This great Truth unto the world he'll tell
None can cure sooner, who cures half so well."

In the spring of 1691, Tom was taken ill and when pressed by his friends to call in medical advice, he refused and declared that he would take no other medicine but his own pills. In spite of his faith in his physic it proved of no avail, and this " benefactor of his species " died on May 12th of the same year. A broadside was printed lamenting this sad disaster, and sung by the ballad-singers about the city.

" Tom Saffold dead ? That famous Operator,
And did no Blazing Star foretell the matter ?
No angry Comet with bright Flames her on,
Foretel the Death of so Renowned a Person ?
Ye ill-bred Stars ye knew when he was living,
He was each day from you some skill receiving,
And could ye not afford one Link Celestial,
To Light him from Black-Fyer's House Terrestial ?
For very well ye flaming lights did know,
'Twas a dark way the Doctor had to go ;
But we alas in vain his absence mourn,

For he is gone, thence never to return.
To's House again, who with his Bills alone
Did fill and furnish half the Town.
So skilled in Drugs and Verse, 'twas hard to show it
Whether was best, the Doctor or the Poet.

His skill in Physick did his fame advance,
Tho' some accuse him of dull Ignorance ;
Powder of post may sometimes do the trick,
As well as Rhubarb, Senna, Agarick,
For let the sad disease be what it will,
The patient's faith helps more than Doctor's Skill ;
Besides he had so quick, so short a way,
No patient under him long grieving lay ;
For was it Fever, Pox or Calenture,
His drugs could either quickly kill or cure.
Sometimes perhaps his Guilded Pill prevails,
But if that fail, the Dead can tell no tales.
What if his medicines thousands Lives should spill ?
Hangmen and Quacks are authorized to Kill.

Ye who now in sweating-tubs devoutly drivel,
Faith Sparks, your Doctor's left you to the Devil.
Howl and lament and shed your briny tears,
Ye *Shadwel* Dames and *Wapping* Wastcoteers
Who blushing with your flasks of water,
Came to his House to understand the matter.
Lament ye Damsels of our *London City*,
(Poor unprovided girls) tho' fair and witty,
Who maskt would to his House in couples come,
To understand your matrimonial doom ;

To know what kind of men you were to marry
And how long time, poor things, you were to tarry ;
Your Oracle is silent, none can tell
On whom his Astrologick mantle fell.
For he when sick refused all Doctor's aid
And only to his Pills devotion paid ;
Yet it was surely a most sad disaster
The SAWCY PILLS at last should KILL THEIR
MASTER."

EPITAPH.

" Here Lyes the corps of Thomas Saffold,
By Death, in spite of Physick, Baffl'd,
Who leaving off his working Loom,
Did learned Doctor soon become,
To Poetry he made pretence,
Is plain to any man's own sense ;
But he when living thought it Sin
' To hide his Talent in Napkin.'
Now Death does Poet, Doctor crowd
Within the Limits of a shroud."
London 1691.

Saffold's business was carried on by John Case, who
removed to his house in *Black-Friers*, but he *gilded* the
old sign of the *Black-ball* and thus announced himself,

" At the *Golden Ball* and *Lillies Head*
John Case yet lives, though *Saffold's dead*."

Case was born at Lyme Regis in Dorsetshire about
1660, and came to London when about fifteen to seek

his fortune. He was a sharp, shrewd youth and fond of reading. He went to lodge at Lambeth and before he was twenty-three published a book called "The wards of the Key to Helmont proved unfit for the Lock, or the Principles of Mr. Wm. Bacon examined and refuted, (London, 1682)."

He described himself at that time, as "a student in Physick and Astrology" and the book shows that he certainly had some literary ability. His friend John Partridge, who had become well-known as the author of Astrological Almanacks, contributed a commendatory preface to the work, which is dedicated "To my esteemed friend Sir Thomas Gery Kt." Their friendship is mentioned later on by Swift.

In 1695, Case published "Compendium Anatomicum nova methodo institutum," a little book which brought him some fame as a medical writer. In it he ably defends the opinions of William Harvey and De Graaf on the "Generation of animals," and the work is so well put together, that it is doubted by some, including Chalmers, that Case actually wrote it.

In the same year he published another book called "Ars anatomica breviter elucidata," and within twelve months his "Flos Ævi or Celestial Observations" was printed.

It was about this time, probably on account of his literary efforts proving unremunerative, he decided to take up Saffold's mantle as a quack-doctor and Lilly's practise as an astrologer, and went to live in the house at Black-Friers, where he hung up his "Golden Ball." He took possession of the apparatus of both his predecessors, and is said to have been especially proud of the darkened room and the collection of mysterious appliances, that had been used by Lilly to impress those who sought his aid and power, to see visions of their departed friends, and to question the oracle as to the future.

Under the sign of the " Golden Ball," over the door, he had these lines inscribed :

> " Within this place
> Lives Doctor Case."

Addison later declared in the *Tatler*, " Case made more money by this couplet, than Dryden made by all his poetical works put together."

Following Saffold's style of poetic bill, he issued this address :

> " Dear Friends, let your disease be what God will,
> Pray to him for a cure, Try Case's Skill;
> Who may be such an healing instrument,
> As will cure you to your Heart's content.
> His medicines are cheap, and truly good,
> Being full as safe as your daily food,
> Case, he can do what may be done, by
> Either Physick, or true As'rology."

" Case offers the Poor, Sore, Sick and Lame, advice for Nothing, and proper medicines for every particular distemper at reasonable rates. He doth also, with great certainty and privacy, resolve all manner of Lawful questions according to the Rules of Christian Astrology, and more than fifteen years experience. He is to be spoken with alone from Eight in the morning till eight at night."

In another bill, he describes himself as " a Spagyrick Physician," and enumerates some of his wonder-working nostrums. These include, his " Mundus Sanitatus, the operations of which are the wonder of the world, price 2s. 6d., very proper. The Pilula Cathartica, the True Medicarem Universale, Gutta Stipitica Miraculum Mundi, the world's wonder for inward wounds, Liquor Diuretica and Analepticus, and the cordial draught or wonderful Elixir."

Around his pill boxes he pasted a label with the words :

" Here's fourteen pills for thirteen pence ;
Enough in any man's own conscience."

In one of his bills Case declares that he was admitted " an approved practitioner in that famous science of physick in 1672, and both before and since, has been an industrious inquirer into the secrets of Spagyrick or Chymical Art. He has a laboratory of his own in this city in the said art and at length by the Blessing of God attained a most noble Universal Medicine, which he has thought fit to call by the name of Mundus Sanitatus."

He concludes :

" He knows some who are knaves in grain,
And have more gall and spleen than brain,
Will ill reward his skill and pain."

A bill issued later is illustrated with a woodcut of an Indian and a Negro boy, busy pounding with a pestle and mortar, while on either side are representations of lancets, forceps, scissors and other surgical instruments.

Good News to the Sick.

Ver again ft *Ludgate* Church, within *Black-Fryers* Gate-way, at *Lillies-Head*, Liveth your old Friend Dr. *Case*, who faithfully Cures the Grand *P—*, with all its Symptoms, very Cheap, Private, and without the leaft Hindrance of Bufinefs. *Note*, He hath been a Phyfitian 33 Years, and gives Advice in any Diftem per *gratis*.

All ye that are of *Venus* Race,
Apply your felves to Dr. *Case*;
Who, with a Box or two of PILLS,
Will foon remove your painfull ILLS.

A BILL OF DR. CASE

In another headed, " Good News to the Sick," he informs the public, that " over against *Ludgate Church* within *Black-Fryer's Gateway* at *Lillies Head,* liveth your *Old Friend, Dr. Case,* who faithfully Cures the Grand P——with all its symptoms, very cheap, Private and without the least Hindrance of Business."

" *Note,* He hath been a Physician 33 years and gives advice in any Distemper per gratis.

> " All ye that are of *Venus* Race,
>   Apply yourselves to *Dr. Case ;*
>   Who with a box or two of *Pills,*
>   Will soon remove your *Painful ills.*"

His bill advertising the " Glorious Spagyrick," is adorned with a picture of Case seated at a table. An angel is descending from a cloud holding a book and bearing the following legend :

> " Strive not for *Gold* nor *Silver*, but with
>   medicines transmute bodies corrupted,
>   into Health."

The bill also has a representation of a shop and laboraory with a skeleton standing by a still.

Case was visited by many fair ladies who were anxious to consult his Oracle, and was no doubt able to furnish them with satisfactory replies to their questions as to the future.

The following skit on one of these consultations, called " A pleasant Dialogue between a Priest and the Oracle," was circulated about the Town.

" Question—'Tell me John Case. Who art thou ?
Answer—' I am the new Dr. Saffold.

Question—' Art thou Dr. Saffold himself or somebody else that resembles him ?

Answer—' It is not permitted to reveal these mysteries.

Question—' How many years wilt thou continue here to give oracle near Ludgate ?

Answer—' More than a dozen.

Question—' Where dost thou intend to go after that ?

Answer—' To White-Fryers, then to Moor Fields, to honour the outskirts of the Town with my presence.

Question—' Are the Oracles of Gadbury, Dr. Partridge and Poor Robin, true Oracles ?

Answer—' Don't desire to know forbidden things.

Question—' What shall I drink when I go from hence ?

Answer—' First Flip, then Cherry Brandy, next Sherry and sugar, next Brandy and Gunpowder, and lastly a dose of Liquid Brimstone to settle your Stomack for Eternity, to prevent any further curdling of Conscience or Paultry pukes of Grace.'"

In his last book, " The Angelical Guide, showing men and women their lott or Chaunce in this Elementary," printed by J. Dawks, in London, 1697, Case confines himself to astrology and fortune-telling, and dedicates the book to " the ingenious Mr. Tryon."

Granger relates a story of a meeting between Dr. Radcliffe and Case. He states, "Dr. Maunby formerly of Canterbury told me, that in his travels abroad, some eminent physician who had been in England, gave him a token to spend on his return with Dr. Radcliffe and Dr. Case. They fixed an evening and were very merry, when Radcliffe thus gave a toast. ' Here's to all the fools, your patients, brother Case!' 'I thank you good brother,' replied Case, 'Let me have all the fools and you are heartily welcome to the rest of the practise.'"

Pope in his "Phrenzy," introduced Case as the doctor, who is summoned to attend John Dennis, and he is also the quack to whom Addison alludes in the *Tatler* in the following mock advertisement.

"Whereas an ignorant upstart in Astrology has publicly endeavoured to persuade the world, that he is the late John Partridge who died 28th March 1708; These are to certify all whom it may concern, that the true John Partridge, was not only dead at that time but continues so to this present day.

" Beware of counterfeits, for such are abroad."

The last bill issued by Case reads thus :

" You noble and ignoble, you may be foretold anything that may happen in your Elementary Adversity, the end thereof.

" Young men may foresee their fortunes and pretty maids their husbands as in a Glass, by this Noble, yea, Heavenly Art of Astrology. This is my last time of publishing bills, therefore be still mindful of the House and Place where ever may be, J. CASE."

Dr. Harris, one of the physicians-in-ordinary to Charles II, relates the story of a quack-doctor, well-known in London at that time as Dr. Pontaeus, whom he states " was the first mountebank who ever appeared on a stage in England."

Pontaeus, who was an audacious fellow, sold an antidote to all poisons which he called " Orvietan," and also a " Green Salve " that he claimed would infallibly heal every wound. He was bold enough to issue a challenge to the physicians of Oxford stating, that "if they would prepare the rankest poison they could contrive, he would undertake that one of his servants should swallow it, and after taking a dose of his " Orvietan," he would recover, and so prove the value of his antidote."

The Oxford physicians took up the challenge and decided the poison should be Aqua Fortis. On the day appointed for the test, a dose was therefore duly prepared and swallowed by the quack's servant on the stage, who at once fell down apparently dead and was carried off by his fellows. The following day however, he appeared again, evidently none the worse for the poisonous draught.

Harris explains, that previous to swallowing the liquid, the man had well greased his mouth and gullet with two or three pounds of butter. After being carried off the stage, Pontaeus dosed him with more butter, and then gave him warm water, which made him sick, and so he soon recovered and was none the worse for the poison.

On another occasion, one of the quack's assistants made pretence to wash his hands in a ladle of molten lead in the presence of the astonished spectators. His hands appeared to be terribly burnt, and he seemed to be suffering great agony. Pontaeus immediately came forward, and applied some of his famous " Green Salve," bandaged them up and led him off the stage. The next day he was again introduced to the audience, and on the bandages being removed, his hands were seen to be quite healed. Pontaeus proceeded to reap a golden harvest from the sale of this wonderful salve.

It transpired afterwards, that the seemingly molten lead was simply warm quicksilver, and the inside of the bowl of the ladle had been painted red. When the man dipped his hands into it, he also had some vermilion secreted between his fingers, which he rubbed over the skin while immersed in the quicksilver, and so duped the spectators.

Orvietan was an antidote electuary, first introduced by a quack into England who came from Orvieto about 1647.

CHAPTER III

A STROLOGY which played such a prominent part in medicine throughout the Middle Ages, as knowledge increased, gradually began to fall into the hands of the quacks.

Until the close of the sixteenth century it had formed part of the regular training of the physician, but as the belief in it waned, the so-called art of casting nativities and fore-telling the future, was seized upon by the quacks and other cunning individuals as an easy way of making a living.

One of the best known astrologers of the early part of the seventeenth century was William Lilly, who was born at Diseworth in Leicestershire in 1602. When little more than a boy, he is said to have tramped to London to seek his fortune and arrived with ten shillings in his pocket. He succeeded in getting service in the house of one Master Gilbert Wright, where, he says, he performed "all manner of drudgeries, such as cleaning the shoes, carrying water and scraping the trenchers."

He remained in London during the visitation of the plague in 1625 and decided to become an astrologer. After devoting several years to the study of the subject and acquiring some knowledge of medicine, he claimed to be able to diagnose disease by the aid of the stars and predict its end.

In June 1644, he published his first book on " Supernatural sight " and " The White King's Prophecy," which was followed by " The Prophetical Merlin," in which he claimed to have predicted the defeat of Charles I at Naseby. He then began to publish annually, his " Prophetical Almanack," through which his name became known throughout the country. From the sale of these books and his successful predictions in " The Prophetical Merlin," he made a great deal of money. Lilly left London in 1665, and deciding to live in the country he eventually settled at Hersham. While there he obtained a licence to practise medicine from the Archbishop of Canterbury. He used to ride to Kingston every Saturday to physic the poor, who flocked to consult him, and to whom he gave his advice and medicines without charge. Owing to the success of his prophecies he came in touch with Elias Ashmole who remained his friend to the end. He died in 1681, and was buried in Walton Church, where a marble slab was placed over his grave by Ashmole, who appears to have been a firm believer in his powers.

Lilly was certainly a very shrewd and quick observer, with a keen eye to read the signs of the times, and this, together with the wide knowledge of human nature he possessed, was no doubt the secret of his success.

He had a warm admirer in a youth named John Partridge, who about 1660, became apprenticed to a shoemaker in Covent Garden and while cobbling, delighted to pore over Lilly's prophetical works.

Partridge, whose imagination was fired by Lilly's success, decided to give up shoe-making for the study of astrology, and in 1680, having as he thought acquired sufficient knowledge, commenced the publication of a regular Almanack which he called " Merlinus Liberatus," and so stepped into Lilly's shoes.

During the reign of James II he journeyed to Holland and is said to have qualified as a doctor of medicine at Leyden in 1689. On his return to London, he married a wealthy widow and resumed the publication of his Almanacks, from the sale of which he drew a considerable income. Swift, under the pseudonym of Isaac Bickerstaff made a mock prediction of his death in a pamphlet, which was said to be written, " to prevent the people of England from being further imposed upon by vulgar Almanack makers."

This was followed by another tract, actually announcing the death of Partridge, and prepared the way for the publication of Swift's famous broad-side :

"An Elegy on the death of Mr. Partridge."

" Here, five feet deep lies on his back
A cobler, star-monger and quack ;
Who to the Stars in pure good will,
Does to his best look upward still.
Weep all you customers that use
His pills, his almanacks or shoes,
Step to his grave but once a week ;
This earth which bears his body's print,
You'll find has so much virtue in't
That I durst pawn my ears, 'twill tell,

What e'er concerns you full as well,
In Physick, stolen goods or Love,
As he himself could, when above."

After this, Partridge had the utmost difficulty in persuading the public that he was *still alive*, while the wits of the Town, including Rowe, Steele and Congreve, took part in keeping up the fiction, by publishing humorous skits and verses, such as the following :

" Strange an Astrologer should Die
Without one wonder in the Sky.
Not one of all his Crony Stars
To pay their Duty at his Hearse."

.   .   .   .

" Some Wits have wondered what Analogy
There is 'twixt Cobling and Astrology,
How Partridge made his Opticks rise,
From a shoe-sole to reach the skies."

Partridge, whose real name was Hewson, however, long survived his obituaries and continued his publications until his death at Mortlake on March 29th 1715. Judging from their numerous bills, astrologers and fortune-tellers multiplied and flourished in London in the time of the Stuarts, and from Lilly and Partridge, down to the lesser lights, drove a profitable trade in fore-telling the future from the stars.

Among the latter was Professor Woodward, who lived at " the sign of the 'Globe,' over against the 'Cheshire Cheese' in Arundel Street, by St. Clement's Church in the Strand."

He heads his bill with the ingenuous legend, " Honest Invitations." He professed to be ready to answer any queries such as the following : " What part of the world, city or country is best to live in ? Life, whether long or short, happy or unhappy ? Servants or Lodgers, if trusty or not ? If good to hire or buy the house, ship, or land desired ? Money owing, if recoverable ? Law suits, who shall overcome ? What manner of person one shall marry ? If attain the office or place of prefer-ment ? " These and many other important questions Woodward was prepared to answer on payment of his fee.

But his activities did not end in fore-telling for in Physick he states, you may also have his advice and he was ready to sell you his " Famous Balsamick Pills," an " infallibly good cure for Scurvy and 33 other diseases," some of which appear to be unknown to us to-day. What for example, was " Sleepy Evil " ? Was it the disease now known as sleepy sickness ?

It was a common practise with many quacks to re-commend the Waters of the mineral springs of which there were several in and around London. Thus Wood-ward recommends those who take his pills, to drink either Tunbridge, Epsom, Islington or other mineral waters, which it is likely did the patient more good than the pills.

Another practitioner was to be found at the " Sign of the ' Flower de Luce,' near the Church-porch in the Little Minories without Aldgate." He describes himself as " A Gentleman, who in his youth was several years a student in Cambridge, hath travelled, and for above thirty-three years spent the greatest part of his Time, in search after the Solid Truth of the Sublime Science of Astrology, in all its Various Parts ; hitherto, for the private satisfaction and diversion only of himself and Intimate friends." He expresses himself now willing to communicate his skill, by giving " a faithful answer to any Lawfull, Serious Demand, within the compass

CONSULTING THE ASTROLOGER
From a woodcut 1670

of the said Art, to calculate Nativities, and impart his knowledge to any Ingenious Gentleman or others who shall desire it."

He adds one instance (out of many) " to prove the usefulness and verity of this Noble Science."

" The greatest Evil that Invadeth our bodies is sickness, to the Cure of which, a certain Knowledge of its cause, nature, countenance, end, etc., with a fit selection of Remedies, and of the time of preparing and administering them is usually necessary. Now this Heavenly Fountain, supplieth us with all this, as manifold experience that fully convinced, not only us, but all the Sons of Urania."

At Bethnal-Green, "by the Watch-house, at the *Blew Ball and Stars* hanging out of the Balcony, about half-a-mile beyond White-chapel Church, Middlesex," lived Dr. Sandford, who styles himself an "Astrological Medicus," who, "with God's Blessing in his long studies and practise in Physick and Astrology, hath obtained most proper experienced Secrets, viz. His most excellent, highly approved "Soveraign Cordial, Cathartick, Universal Purging Pills, which fortify decaying Nature."

"Likewise, he hath prevented many from Danger and Ruine by his timely advice. Calculates Nativities, and at the sight of the afflicted patient, he giveth determinate Judgment on the Disease and whether curable.

"When love or fear shall wound the Patient's Heart,
Some wand'ring Star points out the secret Dart,
Art may give ease, when nothing can expell,
The raging Pain which in the Mind may dwell."

The Quack delighted to deride and score if possible off his rivals, and an instance of this may be quoted from a bill headed "No cheat, nor Meer pretended Fortune-teller, but an Honest and Faithful Student in Astrology," issued by a practitioner who hails from "Lower Moor-fields, over against New Bethlem, at the Corner-House of Long-Alley, where you may see a *Sign* and a *Board* over the Door that signifieth the practice, *although neither Globes or Balls.*"

A BRIEF DISCOVERY OF SOME CHEATS

" Too many have been deceived and cheated of their money by applying themselves to ignorant Professors of Art (or meer pretended Fortune-tellers) of which there are several sorts viz., there are a sort of women and some men, that pretend to fore-tell things by silly Fancies or new Inventions made into books under the names ' The Shepherd's Calender,' ' The Dutch Fortune Book,' ' The Wheel of Pythagoras,' which are all of no more worth or operation than Toys for children.

" A pretended Astrologer (not far from my present abode) hath got considerable summs of money from many ignorant, silly creatures, by promising to do such strange things for them as raise the wind, at other times that he must raise a Spirit (*out upon him for shame*) and to others he'll say, that he hath Rare Secrets which he calls Pentacles and Sigils, but I am sure they will do nothing else but draw money out of people's pockets.

" When this bill comes to the hands of those persons who have been so cheated of their money, if they please come to me, I will (without any reward to myself) set them in a way to get all their money again, without the trouble or charges of commencing a Suit of Law for it. Those that shall pretend to conjure for you or to shew you the Face of the Quesited in a Glass, or to work by charms or Inchantments, are neither Conjurers nor Astrologers, BUT MEER CHEATS.

" Believe in God, his Works do not deride,
    And let the Lights of Heaven be thy Guide ;
The Planets ever were, and will be still
    God's Candles for the Wise to search his Will."

" Are you any ways afflicted ? Come and learn the
best way to be comforted. Are you poor ? Come and
learn how to get riches ? But if you will not believe
the Operations and Effects of God's Handy-Work, sit
still at home, and slug on and receive not the Benefit
of his offers."

The Astrologers and Quacks were particular in their
bills to give explicit directions for finding their abodes,
which was very necessary in the dark, narrow streets
and alleys of the city.

Thus, one living in White-Cross Street in Cripple-gate
Parish, directs his customers :

" Almost at the far end near Old-Street, turning in
by the Sign of the *Black Croe*, in Goat-alley, then
streight forward, *down three steps*, at the *Sign of the
Globe*, you will find one, who hath above Thirty years
Experience, and hath been Counsellor to Counsellors
of several Kingdoms, and hath a secret in Art, far beyond
the reach or knowledge of common Pretenders.

" He practises the most noble Art of Christian Astrology, and telleth the meaning of all magical Pentacles,
Sigils, Charms and Lamens, and with a Glass and
helpth in further marriages.

" He hath attain'd to the Signet Star of the Philosopher. He likewise hath attain'd to the Green, Golden

and Black Dragon, known to none but Magicians and Hermetick Philosophers, and will prove he hath the True and Perfect Seed and Blossom of the Female Fern, all for physicians uses ; and can tell concerning every serious Person, what their business is on every Radical Figure, before they speak one word.

" Secondly, what is past in most of their life ; what is present and what is to come ; where that they have moles, what colour they are and what is the meaning of them."

Here we have a veritable magician indeed, and an adept, who has apparently reached the highest plane of Hermetick philosophy.

Fern seed to which he alludes, was believed to have the power of making the person who carried it invisible.

Shakespeare alludes to the belief in the lines " We have the receipt of Fern seed—we walk invisible." (Ist Henry IV, Act II.)

Writing in the XVIth century, Lyte says in referring to the fern, " a plant so strange, that grows without seed, must needs have strange qualities and it hath the peculiar power of making persons invisible."

In ancient times, when a plant was found to grow and increase but of which the organs of fructification were invisible, it was deemed to have the power of conferring invisibility. This idea was seized upon by the quacks, some of whom claimed to have discovered the unknown seed of the fern, which was supposed to possess this marvellous property.

From an early period there were many superstitions

connected with moles. When on the body they were believed to bring "good-luck" to the individual who had them.

This astrologer concludes with the following lines :

> " To all that please to come he will and can
> Cure most diseases incident to Man,
> The *Leprosie*, the *Cholick*, and the *Spleen*,
> And most diseases common to be seen,
> Although not cured by Quack Doctors proud,
> And yet their Names doth ring and range aloud,
> With riches and with Cures which others do,
> Which they could not perform, *and this is true*.
> This Doctor, he performeth with out doubt
> The *Ileak Passion*, Scurvy and the Gout,
> Even to those the Hospitals turn out."

" He will sell no more of his *Friendly Pills to Nature*, to those that make money of it again. He keeps them for the use of the Poor.
LAUS DEO."

At the *Sign of the Parrot*, opposite to *Ludgate Church*, within *Black-fryer's Gateway*, there dwelt another astrologer, who declares he can fore-tell " anything that may happen to your Elementary Life as to what time you may expect Prosperity, or if in Adversity, the end thereof. Also, young men may foresee their fortunes as in a Glass and pretty maids their husbands, in this Noble, yea Heavenly Art of ASTROLOGY."

One astrologer even claimed to be able to " Tell the

winner " and W. Baynham, the author of the " Royal
Almanack," was ready to inform those who consulted him
beforehand, *Which shall Win in Horse or Foot races.*
He was to be found at the " *Blew Ball* in *St. Andrew's-
street*, being the Corner house over against the upper
end of *St. Martin's-lane*, near the *Seven Dials, St. Giles*,"
and was doubtless well patronised. He claims to be a

AN ASTROLOGER'S BILL

Noble, or Ignoble, you may
be foretold any thing that
may happen to your Elementary
Life: as at what time you may expect Prosperity ; or · if in Adversity, the end thereof: Or when you
may be so happy as to enioy the
Thing desired Also young Men
may foresee their Fortunes·as in a
Glass, and pretty Maids their Hus
bands, in this Noble, yea Heaven
ly Art of ASTROLOGIE.
At the Sign of the *Parrot*, opposite to *Ludgate* Church, within *Black-Fryars* Gateway.

follower of the " Famous William Lilly and a practitioner
of Astrology and Physick.   He tells the Christian
Name and Trade at length, of any Lover or Friend, as
well as their own.
   " How many Husbands they shall have, and whether
man or wife shall die first. He calculateth nativities by
the time of Birth, and in Physick, by an Astrological

Rule, resolving whether the disease will end in Life or Death. As an astrological Professor in its several parts, he undertakes to teach the same to any that desire to understand it, according to the Doctrine of Ptolemy, Regiomontanus and Confalonerius the Learned Monk."

'*A Remarkable Person,*' who was to be spoken with every day in the week from morning till night, " at the *Golden Ball* in *Gulstone-square,* being the next turning beyond *Petticoat-lane, and the next Turning beyond* White-chappel-Bars, the *Third house* in the *Left-Hand* in the Square," claimed to be able to work marvels.

By his travels, he states, "in many Remote parts of the world, he has obtained the " Art of Presaging or Fore-telling, all *Remarkable Things* that ever shall happen to men or women in the whole course of their lives, to the great Admiration of all that ever come to him, and this, by a method never yet practised in England.

"He might give multitudes of examples but offers but these few.

" A Young Woman, who had a person pretending Love to her for many Years ; I told her she would find him false and deceitful to her, and that he never designed to marry her, which was a great trouble to her to hear, by reason she had plac'd her affection on him. But she found it True, for shortly after he married another.

" Soon after, she had several Sweet-hearts at a time, and came to me again for advice ; I told her there was one of those she could be happy with, and describ'd him to her. She took my advice and marryed him, and they prove a very happy couple.

" I have prevented the Ruin of Hundreds of young men and women, by advising them to whom to dispose of themselves in marriage.

" Another, who had been many years plagued with a Bad Husband. I told her in a few months she'd Bury him and marry again very happily, *which she found True.* A woman came to me to know if a relation of hers was alive, that was several hundreds of leagues off. I told her he was dead ; shortly afterwards news came it was so."

This astrologer, in addition to his other remarkable powers, was useful for his detective faculties, for he tells us, " A great parcel of Plate etc. was stolen from a Gentleman in Kent. By my Directions, THE THIEF WAS TAKEN AND MOST OF THE THINGS RE-COVERED.

" Finally, I discover if any persons are under an Evil Tongue or Eye, whereby they have been unfortunate many years, not knowing the reason."

The practise of astrology was by no means confined to the male sex and in the seventeenth century, we find there were many women who also followed the Art.

Among them was a " Gentlewoman, who lived next door to the *Castle Tavern,* without *Cripple-gate,* at a *Scrivener's House,*" who proclaims in her bill, that she is prepared to answer such questions, as " Whether Life may be long or short, happy or unhappy ? A person absent, whether dead or alive ? In what part of the world it is best to live ? Whether one shall be rich or poor, and if rich, when and by what means to attain it. She reports also concerning Husbands, Wives, Children, Ships at Sea, or other things, if true or false.

" If with child, and whether male or female ? What kind of person one shall marry, and whether the sweethearts position be great or small ? " These are but a few of the useful and important questions this " gentle " astrologer was ready to answer for a suitable consideration. Besides fortune-telling, we learn that she sold " all sorts of excellent Medicines, ready prepared, fitted for the cure of all diseases (that are curable) in the bodies of men, women, or children and lastly, she hath a Rare Water which beautifies the Face."

At the *White Hart* in *Grays-inn-lane* near the *Queen's Head* dwelt another oracle called Mrs. Stothard, who besides being ready to answer the usual " lawful questions " specialised in interpreting dreams, and telling the signification of Moles in any part of the Body. Her fee was a very modest one, as she gave her advice for 6d, and directs her customers, " to go up one Pair of Stairs without asking."

The old tradition, that certain occult powers were inherited by a seventh child of a seventh child, has survived until recent times, and this belief was turned to advantage by the quacks.

Thus, a bill announces, that at the *"Sign of the Horseshoe and Crown* in *Castle-street,* near the *Seven Dials* in *St. Giles,* Liveth a Gentlewoman, *the daughter of a Seventh Daughter,* who far exceeds all her sex, her business being very great amongst the Quality ; hath now thought fit to make herself known for the benefit of the public.

" She resolves these questions following :

" As to Life, the best Time of it, past or to come ? Servants or Lodgers, if honest or not ? A Friend, if real or not ? A woman with child or not, ever or likely to have any ? Journies by Land, or Voyages by Sea and the Success thereof ? Law suits, which shall gain the better. SHE ALSO INTERPRETS DREAMS.

" These and all other lawful questions, which for brevity sake are omitted, she fully resolves."

In a curious bill called " The Woman's Prophecy or the Rare and wonderful Doctrines," printed in 1677, the author of which is unknown, are revealed, " a thousand strange monstrous things that shall come to pass before New Year's day next or afterwards." The most curious and desperate Diseases are described, such as " *the Glim-'ring of the Gizzard,* the *Quavering of the Kidneys* and the *Wambling Trot.* Likewise " secrets to restore Beauty and Youth to *Ladies of Fourscore,* make *Usurers Immortal* and *Resolve all Questions,* past, present and to come."

CHAPTER IV

SOME MOUNTEBANKS AND THEIR ZANIES

THE mountebanks who usually sold their medicines from a stage, or a coach when travelling, were generally merry fellows of ready wit and repartee. They relied more on their stentorian voices to sell their nostrums than on bills, and were accustomed to extol their virtues in the most extravagant language in the speeches or addresses they declaimed to the assembled spectators.

With the object of attracting attention, as well as amusing their audience, they were usually accompanied by a " zany " who played the fool. He was sometimes dressed as a harlequin and often created laughter by his antics with a monkey.

The use of a fool to divert an audience, is a custom that goes back a considerable period, and even during lectures of a more serious character, the clown's services were not disdained.

In the ancient and famous Anatomical theatre of the Archiginnasio at Bologna, where lectures and demonstrations were given to the students in the sixteenth century, just above the lecturer's rostrum, near the roof, is a small door let into a panel, large enough to admit the head of a man. According to tradition, when the speaker found his listeners becoming inattentive or somnolent, a fool would suddenly pop his head through the little door, crack a joke to make them laugh and disappear.

In the seventeenth and eighteenth centuries, no mountebank was complete without his "Zany" or "Merry Andrew." The Earl of Rochester thus describes him in one of his poems :

> " Merry Andrew. A stage clown or fool,
>   More blades, indeed, are cripples in their art,
>   Mimick his foot but not his speaking part ;
>   Let them the traitor, or Volpone try
>   Could they——
>   Rage like Cethegus, or like Cassius dig,
>   They ne'er had sent to Paris for such fancies
>   As monsters heads and 'Merry Andrew's' dances."

It was from the quack's method of using such speeches at markets and fairs that in after times, those that imitated the like humorous, jocose language, were styled ' Merry Andrews.'

The name is said to have been originally applied to Doctor Andrew Borde, physician to Henry VIII, who was noted for his ready wit and humour.

Thomas Holcroft has left us a picture of a mountebank he first saw at Wisbeach fair ; and "peeping from behind his curtain, that droll devil his Merry Andrew.

" It was a pleasure so unexpected, so exquisite, so rich and rare, that I followed the ' Merry Andrew ' and his drummer through the streets, almost bursting with laughter at his comicality.

" When he returned to the stage followed by an eager crowd, and ordered by his master to mount ; to see the comical jump he gave, alighting half upright, roaring with pretended pain, pressing his hip declaring he had put out his collar-bone, crying to his master to come and cure it, receiving a kick, springing up and making a somersault ; thanking his master kindly for making him well, yet the moment his back was turned, mocking him with wry faces ; answering the doctor, whom I should have thought extremely witty, if Andrew had not been there with jokes so apposite and whimsical, as never failed to produce roars of laughter."

In an old ballad the quack and his zany are thus described :

" When Quack and Zany thus are met,
  The Imperious Emperick seem to fret ;
  But looking round, the crowd to see,
  Are pleas'd to find such company.
  At last the Zany fetched the Wallet
  Of——no Man e'er knew what to call it ;
  Promiscuous sweeps of Druggist shops
  Made into Plaisters, Pills and slops,
  All mix'd, as you'll hereafter see,
  Up with *Infallibility*."

" As soon as his infallible Jewels are disposed of, he presents you with his ' Jack Pudding,' " says a contemporary writer, " who mounts his hempen fortune, flying like a bird in the air, and when he has fool'd it about half an hour, he promises his mobbish spectators more diversion the next visit, honours them with a gracious nod and comes down; and this the Noble Doctor gives them and his Infallible packet at so small a price as sixpence."

The Infallible Mountebank, was the title of a popular broad-side printed by H. Hills in Black-Fryers near the Water-side.

It is headed with a crude woodcut depicting a typical mountebank on his stage, holding a bill in one hand and leading a monkey with the other. At his feet is his medicine chest and on his right the "zany" is seen emerging from behind a curtain.

> " See Sirs, See here (he cries)
>   A Doctor rare,
>   Who travels much at home,
>   Here take my bills,
>   I cure all Ills,
>   Past, Present and to come;
>   The *Cramp*, the *Stitch*,
>   The *Squirt*, the *Itch*,
>   The *Gout*, the *Stone*, the *Pox*;
>   The *Mulligrubs*
>   The *Bonny Scrubs*
>   And all *Pandora's* Box.
>   Thousands I've Dissected,
>   Thousands new erected,
>   And such cures effected
>   As none e'er can tell,
>   Let the *Palsie* shake ye,

Let the *Chollick* rack ye,
Let the *Crinkums* break ye,
Let the *Murrain* take ye ;
Take this, and you are well.
Come wits so keen,
Devour'd with spleen ;
Come Beaus who sprain'd your backs,
Great Belly'd maids,
Old Foundered Jades,
And pepper'd vizard cracks.
I soon remove
The pains of Love,
And cure the Love-sick maid;
The *Hot*, the *Cold*,
The *Young*, the *Old*,
The *Living* and the *Dead* ;
I clear the *Lass*,
With *wainscot Face*
And from *Pimginets free*,
Plump Ladies Red
Like *Saracen's Head*,
With Toaping *Rattafia*.
This with a jirk
Will do your Work,
And Scour you o're and o're,
Read, Judge and *Try*,
And if you *Die*,
Never believe me more."

In 1676, an unknown writer published an amusing
and "faithful" account of the quacks and mounte-

banks of his time in a pamphlet, from which the following is extracted.

" A Quack Doctor is one of the Epidemical Diseases of this age. Betwixt Ignorance and Impudence an Heterogenious jumble.

" You may call him an Enthusiast in Physick or a Gifted Brother in the knack of healing, a Doctor, a Mountebank, but no Master of Arts, save those of cousenage and Lying, a Pettifogger in medicine that goes to Law with Diseases and plays booty with Death.

" Whoever Trust their Lives in his Hands had need of a large dose of Hellebore, and did not madness Excuse, must forfeit their goods and chattells.

" He pretends to cure all diseases that ever Sin intail'd upon the race of Adam, but in truth a vagrant Mountebank, or a ' Seventh Son,' or an ' Irish Stroaker ' out does him fifty in the hundred ;   for his skill is not so much as a Tooth-drawers, and a Corn-cutter is an Æsculapius to him.

" His looks are enough to make one vomit, and his everlasting impertinent tattle, will either purge your gall with anger or your spleen with laughter.

" He might have liv'd well at his primitive handicraft but extravagance put him upon shifts and idleness, made him abandon his anvil or his loom, his aul or his thimble, and pitch upon this safe and thriving course of pocket-picking, no Jiltor, Legerdemain being nowadays so effectual, as a CATHOLICK PILL or a UNIVERSAL POTION.

" His prime care and greatest trouble is to get the

names of diseases without book and a Bead-role of Ratling terms of art.

" To render himself remarkable, he first prevails with some Associate Porters and Tripe-women to call him Doctor, for his ingenuity in healing kib'd heeles and curing cut fingers with a shoe-maker's Ind and cobwebs. Two gally-pots and a penyworth of Sena stalks set him up, and he is not so soon a Student as a Professor. Impudence is his license to practise and at the seventh Funeral he has caused, he takes his degree. When he comes to ' Let Blood,' you would think him about to stick a Calf, and he thumbs your Pulse like a Carman playing on a lute. When people tell him their grief and their ails, he tells them 'tis a *Scurbattical Humour* afflicting the *Diaphragma*, and then pulling out a box of *Quicksilver Pills* (for his pocket is all his pharmaco-pœia) he bids 'em take them. His ambition is to be counted a Phylosopher by Fire. His Brain-pan, is stuft with *Antimony* and *Vitriol*, but his fairest pretence to chymistry, is because an excellent trick he has got to turn Powder of the Rows of Red-herrings, or a vial of fair water, into good hard silver.

" At first he deals as a private Mountebank and makes every blind Alehouse he comes to his stage, where he tells a thousand lies of his Miraculous Cures, and has his Landlady at his elbow to vouch them.

" He bribes all the nurses he can meet with, and keeps a dozen midwives in his pension to proclaim his skill at gossipings. He indears the chambermaid by a private dose to bring him in with her mistress, the new married Citizen's wife, that outlongs Rachel for a Bantling comes to him, and the Suburb Gammers admire him for topeing a pot so socially.

" Some times knowing his medicines not worth buying, he takes up a humour of giving them away, and pretends to cure all the poor in the three nations for nothing.

" But these are only smaller Angling Baits, his Drawing Net is a Printed Bill which catches the Gudgeons in shoals. For hatching this, he engages some friend that's Book-learn'd to correct the false English and sprucify the sence, and interlard it with Proverbial Latin and Cramp words, as a gammon of bacon is stuft with green herbs and cloaves; then to a confiding printer he goes, who depositing paper and pains, is referred for satisfaction to a snack in the profits and then out comes a *Proclamation of Wonders*, trickt up in some strange form. These impudent ostentatious Decoy-papers he dayly spreads about the London streets, and thereby Lime-twigs the rabble to become his patients. He likewise Hucksters his venome in every market town and village, and if the Farmers would buy it only to treat Rats with it might do them a courtesy.

" His fullest practice is amongst fond women that have more money than wit; he first persuades them that they are not well, and then gives 'um Physick which shall infallibly make 'um sick.

" When persons are killed by his improper applications, he chides their friends for not sending for him sooner.

" The grave covers his ignorance, but if any happen to recover, though but of a cold or an Ague, he magnifies the business as if he had raised a second Lazarus.

" There are so many Fools in the World that a knave can hardly want employment, and they are so incorrigibly silly and stupid, as to think themselves obliged to gratify him for not murthering them, and trumpet him up as the rarest man in the World.

" By these arts he grows famous and rich and buys him the worshipful jacket, and takes State upon him, and defies authority that should suppress his insolency, and at last purchases a Title and arrives at his coach, where we leave him, an instance of Fortunate Folly and Prosperous wickedness, driving on (without repentence) to perfect his pseudo-chymistry in the Devil's Laboratory."

The author concludes by remarking : " it is far from his intention to bespatter the noble art of healing, but 'tis the illiterate and dangerous pretenders that he would expose to deserved contempt.

" If any conscious Dons shall acknowledge the picture to be theirs, and think themselves intended, he frankly tells them, they are the Persons meant indeed."

Some of the speeches of the old mountebanks have been preserved and the following two are fair examples of their style of oratory.

The first is the harangue of Ben Willmore, a notorious quack who had his stage on Tower-hill. Ben arrayed in a scarlet coat, lavishly braided with gold, and a cocked hat with a feather, holding up a little bottle in his hand, would thus address his gaping audience :

" Gentlemen and Ladies,

" Behold this little vial, which contains in its narrow
bounds what the whole universe cannot purchase, if
sold to its true value.   This admirable, this miraculous
Elixir, drawn from the *hearts* of *Mandrakes, Phoenix
Livers, Tongues of Mermaids* and distilled by contracted
Sunbeams, has, besides the unknown virtue of curing all
distempers both of mind and body, that Divine one of
animating the Heart of man to that degree, that however remiss, cold and cowardly by Nature, he shall
become *Vigorous* and *Brave.*

" Gentlemen, If any of you present was at Death's
Door, here's this, my *Divine Elixir*, will give you Life
again.

> ' This will recover whole fields of Slain,
>   And all the Dead shall rise and fight again.'

" Come, gentlemen, buy this *Coward's Comfort*,
Quickly buy !   What fop would be abused, mimick'd
and scorn'd for fear of wounds that can be so easily
cur'd.   Who is it, would bear the insolence and pride of
domineering great men, proud officers or magistrates ?
What foolish heir, undone by cheating gamesters ?

" What Lord, would be lampooned ?   What poet,
fear the malice of his satyrical Brother ?   Come, buy
my Coward's Comfort, quickly buy !

" Here Gent, is my little Paper of Powder whose value
surmounts that of *Rocks of Diamonds* and *Hills of Gold.*
'Twas this made *Venus* a goddess and given her *Apollo.*

" Come, buy it Ladies, you that would be fair and wear

eternal Youth, and you in whom the amorous fire remains, when all the charms are fled ; you that dress young and gay, that patch and paint, to fill up sometimes old furrows on your brows and set yourselves for conquest though in vain. Here's that, which will give you *Auburn Hair, White teeth, Red Lips* and *Dimples* on your cheeks. Come, buy it, all you that are past bewitching, and you'd have handsome, young and active Lovers !

" Come, all you City wives, that would advance your husbands to be Lord Mayors, come buy of me new *Beauty*. This will give it, though now decayed as are your shop commodities ; this will retrieve your customers and vend your false and out-of-fashion wares. Cheat, lye, protest and couzen as you please, a *handsome wife* makes all a lawful gain.

" Here is my famous bottle of Powder, the *Life and Soul of Man*. This is the *Amorous Powder* which *Venus* made and gave the god of Love !

" 'Tis this alone that wounds and fires the Heart, makes women kind and equals men to gods.

" 'Tis this that makes your great Lady doat on the ill-favour'd Fop, your great man be jilted by his little mistress, your politician by his comedian, your chaplain by my Lady's waiting woman—

" In fine Sirs,

' 'Tis this, that Cures the Lover's Pain
And Celia of her cold Disdain.'

" I need say nothing of my *Divine Baths of Reformation*, nor the *Wonders of the old Oracle of the Box*, which resolves all questions which sufficiently declare."

Yet another mountebank, one Tom Jones, was wont to address his hearers :

" Gentlemen and Ladies,

" You that have a mind to preserve your own and your families health, may here, at the expence of a two-penny piece, furnish yourselves with a packet, which contains several things of great Use and Wonderful Operation in human Bodies, against all Distempers whatsoever.

" Gentlemen : because I present myself among you, I would not have you think that I am any upstart *Glister-Pipe*, *Rum-Peeping Apothecary* ; No Gentlemen, I am no such person. I am a regular *Physician* and have travell'd most kingdoms in the world.

" I am not a person that takes delight, as a great many do, to fill your ears with hard words.

" Those Quacks may fitly be called *Solimites*, because they prescribe only one sort of physick *for all distempers*, that is a *Vomit*.

" If a man has bruised his Elbow, *Take a Vomit*, says the doctor.

" If you have any Corns : *Take a Vomit*. If he has torn his Coat : *Take a Vomit*. For the *Jaundice*, *Fevers*, *Flux*, *Gripes*, *Gout*, *Stone* and *Pox*, nay even those Distempers known *only* to my friend the Famous Doctor Tufts, whom you all know, as the *Hockogrocles*, *Marthambles*, the *Moon-Pall* and the *Strong-Fives* : *Take a Vomit*.

" *Tantum*, Gentlemen. These Imposters value killing a man no more than I value drawing an old stump of a tooth, so that I say, They are a pack of *Tag-Rag-Assifetide-Glister-Pipe Doctors !*

" Now Gentlemen, having given you a short account of this spurious Race, I shall present you with my *Cordial Pills*, being the *Tincture of the Sun*. They cause all complexions to *Laugh* or *Smile* in the very taking them, and cure all *Dizziness, Dulness in the Head* and *Scurvy.*

" My *Incomparable Balsam* heals all *sores, cuts* and *ulcers, old* and *new.*

" The next I present you with is my *Specifick*, which certainly Cures all Agues in a minute. The last and most useful medicine prepared throughout the World is this, my *Pulvis Catharticus*. Its virtues are such, it will, equally with the *Unicorn's Horn*, expel the ranke'st *Poison*, 'tis a *perfect* and *speedy Cure* and *fortifies* the *Heart* against all *Faintness.*"

In the following ballad the mountebank thus replies to one who questions his pretensions :

" Stop Sir, you're in error, I am a physician,
   See here's my diploma in good condition ;
   It came by the coach from the North, pon my honour,
   And grateful am I to the generous donor,
   If that wont surfice, Sir, see here is my patent,
   To cure all diseases, apparent or latent ;
   I find you suspected I was but a poacher,
   On other physicians, a fountless encroacher ;
   But my qualification's without the least flaw,
   And I kill my game fairly according to law."

CHAPTER V

LORD BACON in his " Advancement of Learning," observes, " We see the weakness and credulity of men is such, as they will often prefer a mountebank or witch before a learned physician." This was undoubtedly true at the time of the Restoration when the quacks of London increased in considerable numbers, and mountebanks and charlatans thronged to our shores from Germany, Italy, Spain, France and the Low Countries.

From this gallery we must next introduce a famous quack called Cornelius à Tilbourn, who declared he was a " Sworn Chyrurgeon to King Charles II, from whose hands he received a Gold Medal and Chain." It is quite probable that the easy-going Monarch, who had a liking for experimenting with quack remedies, may have patronised Tilbourn. One of his bills is headed with Five coats of Arms and bears the legend " By their Majesties Special License and Authority."

Cornelius first lived at " the *Blue Flower Pot* in Great Lincoln's Inn Fields, in Holbourn Row," where, he says, " you will see at night a light over the door. For the convenience of those that desire privacy, they may come through *Red Lyon Inn*, between the *two Turnstiles* in Holbourn, which is directly against my back door, when you will see the *Sign of the Blue Ball.*" Tilbourn's chief nostrum was the famous *Orvietan* already mentioned, which he sold either in Liquid or in Powder form. This he claimed was "the only *True Orvietan* that expelled that vast quantity of Poyson before King Charles II, for which I received from that Courteous Prince, the Gold Medal and Chain. I dispose of it from half a crown the box, to five shillings, and so what quantity or price you please."

Tilbourn or Tilburg, as he later called himself, went on the principle of "No cure, No money," and was ready to accommodate his patients with food, lodgings and medicines until the cure was performed. He says, "I perform all Manual operations, as the stone in the bladder or kidnies, by cutting or by particular medicines.

"I recover and give sight to the blind. I restore sight in a moment. I cure deafness (if curable). I cure vomiting, rising of the vapours, pain in the milt, stitches in the side and all scorbutick distempers.

"I can, if any person do by accident or misfortune, lose one of his eyes, artificially put in another, not to be discerned as a blemish by any person."

He gives the following account of cures he "lately performed on persons of Quality.

"Sir Richard Greeneway, troubled with the Stone was speedily cured by me. John Owen, Esquire, who so Honourably served his late Majesty in the Dutch Engagements and had five or six ulcerated holes in his leggs, occasioned by splinters, and at first but ill patcht up : in less than six weeks, I made him sound and well. The Lady Ann Seymoure, that had a Lameness in her Limbs, that she was forced to keep her Bed for four years, was cured by me in seven weeks time, and I also cured a cancerated Lip of Sir John Andrews at St James's. Mr. Christopher Shelly hard by *Cupid's Bridge* in Lambeth, was brought to me in a chair, deprived of all his limbs, uncapable of moving hand or foot was (by the blessing of God) perfectly cured by me, to the admiration of all.

" I could mention a great many more which I have cured, but the Paper being too little. VIVANT REX ET REGINA."

From a later bill, we find he had removed to Bruges Street in Covent Garden, " over against the *King's-Play-House* and the *Rose Tavern,* where you will see the *Kings Arms* hang over the Balcony." Here he specialised as an oculist and states, that by his " great Diligence and study, he hath lately found out some Admirable Remedies which was never yet made Publick, for weak or dimm sight occasion'd by Age or otherwise, and bring them to see well without spectacles in a week's time, although they have used them 20 years before." He takes off all " Pearls, Pins, Webbs, Cataracts, both white and black, and skins of all kinds, and gives immediate Sight to those that are termed Stoneblind."

In another bill he styles himself, High German Doctor or Physician, Oculist, Chirurgeon and Rupture Master ! He observes, " that the antient philosopher Plato gives us a proverb for imitation. 'A man that spins out his age idley and not distributing the gifts given him by God Almighty, he ought to be expelled out of the vulgar society of men.' This saying having made deep impression on my mind, I endeavoured to arrive by God's blessing and my weak endeavours to the study of Physick, to know what hath hitherto been hid to others, so that I have obtained to some knowledge more than our forefathers could boast of.

"Now the agreement I make with everyone is, I shall not require one farthing till they have been cured half a year, so well, only I shall require your names and the places of your abode when the half-year is expired. I do cure all Persons that have been at *Venus Sports* of the French, Italian, Indian, High Dutch, English or Spanish variety. If any person hath the scurvy in the mouth or Blacking teeth, I can clean them, although they be black as pitch and make them extraordinary white.

"Master Cornelius à Tilburg now liveth at the *Sign of the Sun* in the Strand, at one Mr. Smith's a Boddice maker, over against the *White Horse Tavern* between *St. Clement's Church* and the *Maypole in the Strand*, where you shall see a candle burning in a Lanthorn out of the window every night."

Cornelius appears to have survived until the time of King William and Mary, for in his last bill headed " By His Majesty's Special License and Authority " he says that he is now " Priveledg'd by our Gracious Sovereign Lord and Lady, King William and Queen Mary, as for several years past he has cured Thousands of People in and about the City of London of dangerous maladies and distempers, who are now living monuments of the Blessings of God by the incomparable vertue of my excellent and never-failing remedies. His House is now at the Sign of the *King's Arms* in Bridge-street, Covent Garden, at the corner of White Hart Yard, exactly over against Exeter-street end at the *Two White Twisted-Posts*. He is the Sworn Chirurgeon to our Sovereign Lord King William, and now for the convenience of the City and some remote parts of the Town, he has taken lodgings at Mr. Berrymans, a grocer and chocolate-maker at the Corner of Angel Court, next door to the Sign of the *Crown* in Bishopsgate-street, over against the *Queen's Head* Tavern within the Gate, where he is to be seen three days a week, and where he still disposes of his famous Orvietan, and hopes this Famous City is sufficiently satisfied in the ability and care

of Your Loving Friend and servant

CORNELIUS à TILBURG."

Another member of the family appears to have succeeded to the business of Cornelius, for a few years later a bill was issued by a Doctor James Tilburg, embellished with a portrait holding a pair of forceps in his hand.

He declares that he is " Famous through Germany and Holland, Brabant, France and Italy and is now living at the *Black Swan* in St. Giles in the Fields, over against Drury-lane end, where you shall see at night, *Three Lanthorns* with candles burning in them upon the Belcony. He may be spoke with, all alone, from 8 of the clock in the morning till 10 at night, desiring you to be careful for your own benefit *not to mistake the place*, because there is a new person that is lately come over, and hath presumed to make use of the bill and Peice which I did formerly make use of."

James Tilburg gives notice that he is " a very expert,

DR. JAMES TILBURG
From a woodcut on his bill

famous outlandish Doctor and Citizen of Hambourgh, and now arrived in London, and hath brought a wonderful Art with him, which he hath found through long seeking-for and travelling through many Kingdoms.

" First, He cures the French Pox, with all its dependents. Secondly, He takes away all pains in the shoulders arms and bones, therefore all ye that are troubled, come to him before you are spoiled by others, for this secret art was never heard of or seen by any as by him.

" Fourthly, If any have anchored in a strange harbour, fearing to have received damage, let them come to him.

" Lastly. He helps them that have lost their Nature and cherishes up the sad'ned spirits of a Marrye'd man, by what occasion soever they have lost it, and does quicken them again as a Rose that hath received the Summer's dew."

Another quack celebrated in the time of Charles II was Will Atkins, who extolled the virtues of his wonderful remedies for gout and sold them in considerable quantities. He lived in the Old Bailey, and his remarkable appearance when he took his walks abroad to visit his patients, always attracted attention. He affected an enormous three-tailed wig, which was frizzled and combed over each ear, and sometimes carried a cane, but he never wore a hat, so as not to disarrange his artificial head-gear.

His appearance is described in the following lines :

. . . . " to make him look more big,
Had on a large, grave, decent, three-tailed wig ;
His clothes full-trimmed, with button holes behind,
Stiff were the skirts, with buckram stoutly lined,
The cloth-cut velvet, or more reverend black,
Full-made and powder'd half-way down his back."

He declared that the curative effects of his nostrums were due to the fact, that each contained at least *thirty different drugs, all of which* were calculated to ease the complaint.

"At the *Angel and Crown* in Basing-lane, being the second turning on the left hand in Bread-street from Cheapside, dwelt a Physician, a graduate in the University of Oxford and a member of the College of Physicians in London," who issued a bill which states that, " he has a pill prepared with wholesome ingredients and of such great vertue, that it ought not to be concealed. These pills will take away all scabs in the head and face and pains in the head, Arms or Legs and prevent much danger, and are to be bought at my House in Basing-lane in boxes from 1s. 6d."

"An Oxford doctor" who heads his bill with a Greek quotation, combined the art of healing with that of a pedagogue and states, that his " *Oxon Pills* against the Scurvy, Dropsie and Colt Evil, exceed all other medicines and are Sixpence a box.

" He draws teeth or stumps with ease and safety. He lets blood neatly and Issues or Setons he curiously makes, for two-pence each and welcome ! "

He also teaches, " writing, arithmetick, Latin, Greek and Hebrew, at reasonable rates by the great, or Twopence, each of them by the week." He concludes with the appeal to the reader to:

" RAPAIR TO THE OXFORD DOCTOR AT THE FLEET PRISON, near Fleet-bridge, London. *Lately a Fellow of Arx-cercer Collge* (!) *Oxon.*"

Among the quacks who congregated in the neigh-

bourhood of the Tower, was Doctor Trigg, who claims
to be the inventor of the famous " Golden Vatican
Pills." In a bill issued from his house on Tower Wharf
he adjures the reader, to " be not so injurious to thyself
as presently to commit this paper to the worst of offices.
It designs thy good, therefore first Read (three minutes
perform the taske) after which use thy discretion.

There were few diseases, according to Trigg, the
Vatican Pills could not cure from Scurvy to Ague.
" They will keep their virtues many years, *even the age
of man*. They may be conveyed to any plantation
without the least danger of decay, and are made up in
Tin boxes and seal'd with the Doctor's own seal, containing 20 for 2s."

According to a manuscript of the XVIIth century
the Vatican Pills were made as follows :

" Take, Anise, Mastich, Ginger, Cardamoms, Cinnamon, Zedoary, Mace, Cloves, Saffron, Aloes wood,
Turbith (yellow sulphate of mercury) Manna, Senna,
Cassia, Mirabolams, of each one drachm, Rhubarb one
ounce, Aloes two ounces, Scordium half drachm. Mass
with Syrup of Roses.

" Smith, an Apothecary at the Sign of the *Three
Black Lyons* in the Old Bailey makes them."

An Italian quack named Salvator Winter from the City
of Naples, who took up his residence at the " *Sign of St.
Paul's Head*, in New King-street, between Long-acre and
St. Giles-in-the-fields, near Covent Garden," solemnly
declares in his bill, that he is " *Ninety eight* years of age

yet by the Blessing of God, finds himself in health and
as strong as anyone of Fifty." He attributes the first to
God and the second to his " Elixir Vitae," which " he
always carries in his pocket a dayes, and at night under
his pillow." When he finds himself " distempered, he
taketh a Spoonful or two, according as need requireth."

There was apparently no disease under the sun that
his " Elixir Vitae " would not cure, from all sorts of
catarrhs to French-pox and Consumption, in fact he
states, that his " Elixir hath such Force and Vigour
that if it were possible it would *revive the Dead*, were
that not a secret reserved to God only."

He tells us, that his " Sovereign Remedy, contains
sixty-two ingredients in its composition, one correcting
the other," thus carrying on the belief common in his
time, that the more drugs contained in a preparation the
surer the cure. Of the miraculous cures he has performed with it " in divers parts of Europe, Particularly
of this Kingdom, he need only mention one viz. The
Most Learned and Honourable of Worthy memory,
Sir Kenhelm Digby, who styles in his book the ' Miraculous Elixir Vitae ' which never doth harm, but
assuredly doth good." Salvator concludes by saying,
that a report is abroad " THAT HE IS DEAD, but he
wishes it to be known THAT HE IS VERY MUCH
ALIVE and of so great an Age."

An old tradition that certain medicines would do more
harm than good if taken during the Dog-days, is turned
to account by Nathaniel Merry, a quack who styles
himself a " Philo-chym and who has lived at *The Star*
in Bow-lane, next but one to the Half-Moon Court for

eight years!" In a friendly and seasonable warning he issues concerning the Dog-days, he states " His ' Archael' or Vital Medicines are truly adapted for all times, being divested of their Crudities and Heterogene Qualities by a true separation of the pure from the impure, and impregnated with beams of Light.

" Such medicines I have always by me faithfully prepared by my own hands. There are many that perish in and about this City, through an evil custom arising from a false opinion, ' That it is not safe to take Physick in the extreams of Heat and Cold or in the Dog-days.'

Nat further claims to have discovered a Cure for the *Dogmatical Incurables.*" " First cure the subjects of their diseases," he says, " and then thou shalt happily cure thy patients of their sicknesses.

" All true medicine is the uncorruptible and undigestable part latent in their subjects, whence it follows, that execrements and foods are no physick or very improper medicines, hence a necessity of separation.

" I have cured when the Body hath been drawn double and fixt so, and the neck and face, drawn and fixt, looking over one shoulder, and have saved many hands, arms, legs, fingers, and toes from cutting off, when they have been ready and order'd for amputation by the vulgar way. My cures have been wrought by medicines, truly adapted and naturally gifted with a capacity to expel and correct venoms and close with nature centrally, by Rays and Beams of Light upon the Spirit of Life, which corrects the Disorder of the Archaeus and reunites its powers.

" All honest Chyrurgeons, Apothecaries and Doctors,

that are not furnished with such medicines and make conscience of the lives and limbs of their patients, may have them of me.

"I will call God to witness, I am Master of such medicines prepared by mine own hands, as the cures I have performed do prove."

James Wasse, who describes himself as "a Citizen and Surgeon of London," and claims to have had Forty years experience; declares that "being himself now Infirm by Age, and not capable of doing his accustomed service to Mankind, he is retiring to the country for his Health, and therefore is resolved to publish the Virtues, Use and Dose of his famous 'Elixir.'"

"This Noble Medicine," he says, "has by the great industry and pains of the author, been brought to that Perfection, that no medicine hitherto made, has answered the ends of this Composition."

Its special virtue was to give "immediate ease to such as are troubled with gravel of any sort, also as an antidote against all contagious diseases, either on Ship-Board or on Shore, caused by corruption of the Air, by bad provisions or any means whatsoever.

"This Noble Medicine is to be had at the Author's own House in *Church-Alley* in Clements-lane, Lombard-street, also at several Coffee-houses like Brightman's, near Wapping Old Stairs, Ive's in St. Bartholomew's-lane. Oliver's at Westminster hall, Roe's at the Bridge-foot and the Admiralty Coffee-house over and against Whitehall."

The mechanical art connected with surgery was not neglected by the quack, and at the "*Crown and Golden*

Ball on London Bridge, next door to the Coffee-house, near St. Magnus' Church," lived H. Hippen, whose speciality was the cure of ruptures. He announces that, " by the blessing of God on his great study, Travels and Experience, he hath at last attained to that, which many of our Forefathers of the same profession have sought for, but never so completely found, as (God be praised) he hath ; and has had wonderful success in cure of diseases." Hippen says, he would not have his patients think that he aims at high prices or makes it his business to get great store of money. " No, in truth he is none of those, and he will give you to understand his Terms (which are very reasonable) before he undertakes you, that you may not be cheated. This then is his agreement with all his afflicted patients ; he takes no money for his trouble or medicines, till a quarter of a year after the cure is performed, and then, as a reward for the same, he requires the sum of Forty shillings or for those who are not able, Thirty shillings.

" FOR THOSE THAT HAVE NO MONEY AND DESIRE IT FOR GOD'S SAKE, HE WILL CURE GRATIS." What more indeed could man offer ?

Patients are finally adjured, to " defer not the Time but come to him before it is too late."

Giovanni Francesco Borri the Italian alchemist, who practised at several of the Courts of Europe in the XVIIth century, but who was eventually thrown into prison and died in the Castle of St. Angelo in Rome, was the originator of several famous medicines. Among them was a " Sovereign Julep," for which marvellous properties were claimed. This wonderful remedy was sold at Morandi's Chocolate House in Playhouse Yard in Drury Lane.

Morandi, who was evidently a compatriot, states in a bill, that " the ' Sovereign Julep ' is universally esteemed in most parts of Europe as well as the Whole World, as being first made and rightly prepared by that most Eminent physician Shavillier Borri, lately deceas'd. A Nobleman in his travels got the Receipt (from the aforesaid Shavillier) for the benefit of his country ; but lately coming into England, has not only here generously given it, as a mark of his favour to a particular Friend, but has also taught him how to make the same."

The Julep was declared to be " an infallible cure for Consumptions, Ptisicks (chest troubles), Asthma's, Catarrhs and all other Distempers whatever afflicting the lungs," and was to be had at Half a Crown a bottle.

Among the army of German quacks that invaded London about this time, was an anonymous " gentleman," who describes himself as a " German Doctor and Surgeon," who took up his quarters at the *Boot and Spatterdash*, next door but one to the *Vine Tavern* in Long-acre, near Drury-lane.

The " Vine " was a famous hostelry in the XVIIth and early part of the XVIIIth century, much frequented and used as a meeting place by many of the celebrated physicians of the time, and is mentioned by Sir Samuel Garth in his poem " The Dispensary."

The German Doctor of *The Boot and Spatterdash* claimed to be a great healer, " who by the Blessing of God on his great pains, travels and experience, hath had wonderful success. He can " Recover and give sight to the blind *in a moment*, cure Hair-lips in *six days*, and the Cancer in the breast or any other part of the body.

" If any woman be unwilling to speak to me, they may have the conveniency of speaking to my wife, who is expert in all women's distempers. As to gouty pains or shrinking of the sinews, I dare presume, few have arriv'd to the perfection in this cure as myself."

The quacks who specially appealed to the deaf were innumerable but prominent among them was Edmund Searl, who lived at *Pye Corner*, over against the *Golden Ball* by West Smithfield.

The whole Searl family appear to have been in the business and the last descendant Margaret, wife of the late Samuel Searl, was famed for relieving and curing deafness.

Margaret says, that " her father practised this art about 38 years and communicated the secret to her only, who practis'd it with him in his lifetime." In her bill she states, that " she is still to be found at *Pye Corner* (although it is reported that I was dead by some pretenders to deceive the World) where I am ready, upon any occasion of the nature to serve such as apply themselves to me, being the survivor of my father Edmund Searl, and of my late husband, Samuel Searl."

Among the quack medicines popular at this period, the *Elixir Magnum Stomachicum* took a prominent place. It was made and prepared by one Richard Stoughton, an apothecary who had a shop in Southwark, known as the *Sign of the Unicorn*. This Elixir was said to be the great remedy for all distempers of the stomach, " Fifty or sixty drops of which (more or less as you please) were to be taken in a glass of Spring water, Beer, Ale, Mum, Canary, White wine, with or without sugar, and a dram of brandy, as often as you please.

" 'Tis most excellent in Tea, in Wine, very pleasant and proper, and in Beer or Ale, makes the best Purl in the world, and Purl Royal in Sack, giving all of them a fragrant smell and taste, far exceeding Purl made with wormwood and now used to drink in their wine at Taverns."

Purl, a drink, now almost forgotten, was the name given to a liquor, made by infusing wormwood or other bitter herbs in ale or beer, while Purl Royal, was a similar infusion made with wine. It was generally taken in the morning, or as an *apèratif* before a meal, to induce a good appetite.

Pepys in his Diary (Feb. 19th 1659-1660) alludes to " a draft of Purle," and as late as 1865, Charles Dickens refers to Purl in " Our Mutual Friend."

Stoughton says that the country doctors and practitioners discountenanced his Elixir, which he claims to be one of the best and most useful medicines that ever was made. " I refer you to them for your purging Physick, but not to mountebanks and such illiterate fellows. The Elixir has *twenty-two* ingredients unknown to any one but me, and has now obtained a great reputation throughout England, Scotland, Ireland and the plantations beyond the Sea."

Stoughton had a keen eye to business, for he concludes his bill thus, " If any Captain or Seaman, Bookseller, Stationer, Shop-keeper, Coffee-man, or any keeping a Publick House, wants any quantities to dispose of or sell again, they may be furnished with good allowance by letter or otherwise."

John Choke, who is said to have served as a major in the Army, and afterwards called himself an " approved physician and further priviledged by His Majesty," was a well known quack who practised in the Strand. He kept two assistants called Blewton and Bemston whom he used to send about the country to sell his nostrums.

Like others of his kind, who found that cant made a never-failing appeal to the public, he heads his bill with the legend :

"NOTHING WITHOUT GOD,"

He then proceeds to extol the virtues of his "*Elixir Capitalis totius Mundi* or the *only Elixir in the World* for the Morow-Cure of the Gout, Dropsie and Agues of all sorts, Tertian, Quartan and Quotidian.

" All these diseases," he says, " I cure infallibly (*by the assistance of God*) in a very short time. I am sensible that the vulgar will not admit that there is any cure for the gout, neither have they any reason, seeing that there are so many pretenders that come short."

Choke states that his wife was a daughter of Baptista van Helmont the famous Dutch physician and chemist, and from him, he obtained the recipe for his wonderful arcana. He further observes, that one " Thomas Odored, unto whom His Majesty recommended a patient of the Falling-sickness, adding, that (' he was perswaded that he could cure him') was his pupil, and he wrote a book, which is no idle pamphlet but dedicated to the

most Reverend Father in God, Gilbert, by Divine
Providence, Lord Archbishop of Canterbury."

"It is needless to declare my forrain actions," he
continues, "and the many thousand cures I have perfected in London. I cured the Duke of Buckingham
of an ague when all physicians had left him, and his
Majesty was pleased to send for me, and as a mark of
his Royal pleasure, gave me his authority to practise
in any of his Dominions without any control."

Choke, who was a fervent Royalist, concludes his bill
with the words

GOD SAVE THE KING.

In a later bill "Major" John Choke describes himself as "the great traveller and one of His Majesty's
Chymists," and extols the virtues of his "most famous
and in a manner, *Miraculous Necklaces*, for easing children in breeding teeth and cutting them without pain.

"The best time to put them on is when they are two
months old and to wear them until they have bred all
their teeth, and none are troubled with the Evil or
Falling sickness."

Choke says that he has not appeared in print, "but
for the good of such as have not much money to lay
out upon Physick, and such persons as can make appear
that they are really poor, he will cure gratis. He
lodgeth at the *Blew Boar's Head and Chequer* in the
Strand, an Oyl shop, between St. Clement's Church and
the Maypole, near the *Greyhound Tavern*, where he
may be spoken with every morning till ten or eleven
a clock."

" The names of the parents of children that have made use of the Virtuous Necklaces are, the Countess of Northumberland, Lády Bartees at St. James's, Lord Burleys, Sir William Drake in Bucks, Sir Edward Turner in Essex, Mrs. Grooms in Windmill-street near Pickadilly, Mrs. Flowers in Pye-alley in Fan-church street and others."

The Anodyne Necklaces as they were sometimes called, remained in use down to the middle of the XVIIIth century.   Among Choke's rivals and successors, was Burchell of Long Acre, who says they were invented by Dr. Tanner and recommended by Dr. Paul Chamberlen, a descendant of the family of famous Man-midwives.   He states that the " Virtues of the same being so large, I thought fit as in duty and was bound to my fellow Christians, to revive this worthy Anodyne from the ashes which hath been advantageous to all mankind.   Being not much bigger in weight than a Nut-meg, absolutely easeth all children in Breeding and Cutting of teeth without pain ; and also children that have so worn them, have been stronger at nine months than them of twelve.

" They are sold for the publick good for five shillings each necklace, by fifty people, including Mrs. Pope, a Perfumer at the *Pope Head*, Mr. Searson at the *Maiden Head and Castle* in Pickadillee, Mr. Gyles at the *Black Raven*, backside of St. Clement's Church near the May-pole, Mr. Oxspring at the *Hand and Shears* in Shoo-maker row, Black-fryers and others."

The beads of these necklaces were said to be made of peony wood, which curiously enough, was recommended by Oribasius the Roman physician in the fifth century, to be worn round the neck to prevent epilepsy. Like any other hard substance given to infants to bite, they no doubt helped to cut their teeth.

More a charm than a medicine, were the small bags sold to hang around the necks of children to prevent rickets which are thus advertised in the *Intelligencer* in 1664.

" Small Baggs to hang about Childrens necks, which are excellent both for the prevention and cure of Rickets, and to ease children breeding teeth are prepared by Mr. Edmund Buckworth and constantly to be had at Mr. Philip Clarks, Keeper of the Library in the Fleet and nowhere else at 5 shillings a bagge."

CHAPTER VI

FOREIGN QUACKS AND NEW DISEASES

THE quack of old seized every opportunity to abuse his rivals and so extol his own learning and superiority as a healer. An instance of this may be quoted from a bill headed, " A CAUTION TO THE UNWARY " issued by E. Gray, who styles himself, " A Doctor in Physick, one of His late Majesties Physicians, above twenty years since Fellow of King's College in Cambridge, and now at the *Golden Ball* in Hatten-garden, near Holbourn."

" 'Tis generally acknowledged throughout all Europe," he says, " that no Nation has been so fortunate in producing such eminent Physicians as this Kingdom of ours, and 'tis as obvious to every eye, that no country was ever pestered with so many *ignorant Quacks* and *Empericks*.

" The Enthusiast in Divinity, having no sooner acted his part and had his Exit, but on the same stage, from his shop (or some worse place) enters the enthusiast in Physick ; yesterday a Taylor, Heel-maker, Barber, Serving-man, Rope-dancer, etc, to-day *per saltum*, a learned Doctor, able to instruct Aesculapius himself, for *he* never obliged mankind yet with a Panacea, a Universal Pill or Powder that could cure all diseases, which now every post can direct you to do, though it proves only the Hangman's Remedy for all diseases by Death.

" *Pudet haec opprobria dici,* for shame my dear countrymen, re-assume your reasons, and expose not your bodies and purses to the handling of such illiterate fellows, who never had the education of a Grammar school, much less a University.

" Nor be ye so irrational as to imagine anything extraordinary (unless it be ignorance) in a pair of out-landish Whiskers, though he is so impudent to tell you, he has been Physician to Three Emperours and Nine Kings ; when in his own country, he durst not give physick to a cobler.

" Nor be ye gull'd with another sort of Impostor, who allures you to him with ' Cure without money,' but when once he has got you into his clutches, he handles you so unmercifully as he does unskilfully.

" Nor be ye imposed on by the pretence of any *Herculean Medicine,* that shall with four doses, at 5s. a dose, cure the most inveterate Pox, a distemper not to be eradicated (in the opinion of the most learned in all Ages) with less than a renovation of all the humours in the whole body.

" These and the like abuses, have induced me to continue this publick way of Information, that you may be honestly dealt with and perfectly cured, by repairing to *him* who, with *God's Blessings on his studies,* and *twenty years successful practice* in this *City of London,* hath attained to the *easiest and speediest ways of Curing.*"

The quacks were always eager to make excuses for

endeavouring to obtain publicity, by advertising the virtues of their remedies and proclaiming their skill. Thus " J.T.," a practitioner who calls himself a " Licensed Physician " and " who liveth in the Upper Moorfields at the *Globe and Two Balls*, addresses himself in recommending his *Pilula Imperialis vel Sospitalis*, whose vertues and Excellent Qualities do aloud proclaim to the world, the great benefit they bring to mankind, they being the only Antidote against the French Scurvey.

" Courteous Reader. Were it not to gratify the important solicitations of several friends and gentlemen, who does well know what strange cures, even to admiration, my Pills have done to divers persons, I should not have taken this publick way to Practice, but as we were not altogether born for ourselves, I have exposed these my medicines to the Publick, so they may infallibly find a safe and speedy cure, and that without being Grip't too hard in the Pocket."

Dr. Lionel Lockyer, a famous quack in the time of the Commonwealth, who made a great deal of money from the sale of his pills, was buried in St. Saviour's Church, Southwark in 1672. His tomb has his effigy in stone, representing him dressed in a long furred gown, wearing a large flowing wig, and on a pillow on which he reclines resting on his elbow, is the following inscription:

" Here Lockyer lies interr'd, enough ; his name
    Speaks one hath few competitors to fame ;
    A name so great, so gen'ral it may scorn
    Inscriptions which do vulgar tombs adorn
    A diminution 'tis to write in verse

His eulogies, which must mens mouths rehearse,
His virtues and his Pills are so well known,
That envy can't confine them under stone.

But they'll survive his death, and not expire
Till all things else, at th' Universal fire!
This verse is last, his pills embalm him safe
To future times, without an Epitaph."

Lockyer issued a pamphlet in 1670, in which he relates the wonderful cures wrought by his " Pilulae Radiis Solis Extractae." Seventy-four cases are described, including that of a man " who thought ill of the pills after taking one box."

" All such these," he says, " may keep their money and their diseases too." He then cites the case of a man who was left incurable but was " cured of a Regiment of diseases and only by these pills."

Another cunning quack who hails from the " *Sign of the Water Tankard* in Northumberland-alley in Fanchurch-street, near Aldgate, *there being Pales before the window*," has the distinction of having invented a new name for a complaint very common in the XVIIth century. This disease, variously known as *Morbus gallicus*, *Morbus anglicus* and other terms, he designates as the *Affection Allamode*, which he says he has made it his business in his studies and practice, " to find out means more effectual than the common ways, which *by God's assistance with his endeavours*, he has attained to a most expeditious, safe and easie method."

The quack doctor's bills enumerated so many common diseases that it was thought by one ingenious practitioner it was time some new ones were invented. Dr. Tufts, who announces from the *Three Compasses* in Maiden-lane, that he has newly arrived from his travels, "states that after forty years study, he hath discovered *Several strange Diseases*, for which (*though as yet not known to the world*) he hath *infallible cures*. "Now the names of these new Distempers are :

THE STRONG FIVES, THE MOON PALL, THE MARTHAMBLES, AND THE *HOCKOGROCLE*.

" Although the Names, Natures, Symptoms and several cures of these *New Diseases are altogether Unknown to our greatest Physitians*, and the particular knowledge of them would (if conceal'd) be a vast advantage to the aforesaid person ; yet he, well knowing that his country's good is to be prefer'd to his private interest, doth hereby promise all sorts of People, a faithful cure of all or any of the Diseases aforesaid, at as Reasonable Rates as our modern Doctors have for that of any common Distemper."

Here is a most ingenious and artful idea, and it is a wonder that some of the quacks of our own time have not adopted it. One can imagine the advantage it would give to the discoverer, who might not be so disinterested as the worthy Tufts.

Are you suffering from the *Marthambles*, Consult Doctor X——, for he alone will have the requisite knowledge to cure you, or should you have the *Hockogrocles*, the man who discovered them is surely the only one who can put you right.

" DEO ADJUVANTE " was the motto of a " Doctor of Physick well-known for his successful practice in the City of London, who lived in the Haymarket by Charing-cross, at the sign of the *Half Moon*, next the *Nag's Head Tavern*, being the *Balcony Room*, one pair of stairs," who claimed to have " an admirable skill in urines, though Ignorants dispise it, yet from which the Learned know the truest Indications of occult diseases."

He was a pioneer in the treatment of tubercular disease and neurasthenia, by means of fresh air and change, for he announces, that " For melancholy persons inclining to distraction or such that are consumptive, he hath a Large Country House with Gardens, being excellent Air, within a mile of the Town, where the doctor is daily to give advice and what physick is most necessary for recovery, at easie rates."

It is curious how the quack, with his empirical knowledge, sometimes stumbled on a treatment that proved of great value centuries afterwards.

The quack who delighted to pose as a friend to his patient and who announced that he had acquired his skill and wisdom from some mysterious source, appears always to have had an attraction for the public. Of this type was the " Licensed and Legal Practitioner in Physick and Surgery" of the *Globe and Urinal*, at the Corner House next the Square in Baldwin's Gardens near Holbourn, the third turning from Leather-lane and the third from Gray's Inn."

He declares, that " he has practis'd thirty years and travelled twenty-seven years through several kingdoms and Provinces, and in the year 1680 was at Leghorn in

Italy, where he obtained of an old Italian Physician the knowledge of the " Famous Arconum Pill, which he doth assure is free from mercury and is a perfect cure for morbus gallicus." He describes himself as *A Friend to the Diseased* and his remedy, which also cureth the Scurvy and all Rheumatick pains, may be taken in any season by Sea or Land.

" Take notice, in short, that this artist Cureth all diseases curable in the Bodies of men, women, and children, and he is the *only man in Town* for curing the King's Evil, Cancer and Ulcers.

" He can also take away all Webs, Pearls, Spots, Sparks, Clouds and films from the Eyes, and coucheth cataracts if occasion be." One wonders how many of his unfortunate patients he thus may have blinded ?

Another quack of foreign origin who flourished in London at this time, was " The Gentleman from Louvain," who was to be found at the " Sign of the *Moon and Stars* in Leopard's-court in Baldwin's Gardens near Holbourn, from 8 in the morning till 7 at night." This " Gentleman," who " by the benefits of a learned education in the University of Louvain, daily study and thirty years practice and travels " declares, that he has arrived at a greater Perfection in several Arts than the common practitioners in Physick can justly pretend to. " To strangers that cannot speak English, through his learning he is able to speak to them in Latin or French."

His wife was also in the business, and " sells excellent beautifying washes at 1s. the bottle, and has proper remedies for distempers incident to the female sex." His " Cephalick Powder " he claims to be " a present remedy for all diseases of the head proceeding from colds or excess of humours, Price 6d. a paper," and he concludes his bill as follows :

> "Would you your minds free from each labouring
>   doubt,
>   The future state of your Disease find out ?
>   The WHEN and HOW of things to come explore,
>   Shall you grow rich (or God forbid) be Poor ?
>   Are you fall'n sick or grievous pains endure ?
>   He'll tell the Best and Speedi'st way to cure.
>   If good to marry, if the charming Soul
>   That wounds your Heart, will ever make it whole ;
>   Ask but the Doctor, you shall truly know
>   What in each thing the ruling Stars will do."

" *Note*. This is the same doctor that liv'd in *Globe court* and after in *Hanging-Sword-court* in *Fleet-street*. Those that can procure the time of their birth are desired to bring it with them, because some questions are best answer'd and some diseases best discover'd, by the Party's nativity."

Don Lopus, the "Illustrious Spanish Doctor," who declared that he had just arrived from the ancient City of Saragossa, was a mountebank with a sense of humour. Accompanied by his Zany and assistants, he would thus address his audience:

"Most noble Gentlemen and egregiously beautiful and virtuous Ladies, with the rest of my friends and auditors. Behold your humble and most officious Servant, Lopus, who has come on purpose to make you a present of his Physical and Chymical Arts to your fair acceptance, and especially his most inestimable Vegetable and highly valued *Oil*, which I protest, I and my six servants are not able to make so fast as it is fetched away from my Lodging by Gentlemen of your City. Strangers of the Terra firma and worshipful merchants, ever since my arrival and have detained me to their uses by their splendidous liberalities and worthily. For what avails your rich man to have his magazines stuft with Moscadelles of the purest grape, when his physicians prescribe him on pain of Death, to drink nothing but Water cocted with aniseeds ?

"O' Health ! Health ! the Blessing of the Rich.

"The Riches of the Poor ! Who can buy thee at too dear a Rate, since there is no enjoying this world without thee. Be not so sparing of your purses honourable gentlemen I entreat ye, as to abridge the natural course of Life.

"This is the Physician. This the Medicine. This counsels. This Cures. This works the effect ; And in sum, both together may be term'd an abstract of the Theorick and Practick in the Æsculapian Art.

"Now Zan Fritada, prithee sing a verse extempore in Honour of it."

The Zany's song :

"Had old Hippocrates or Galen,
    (that to their books put med'cines all in)
    But known this Secret, they had never
    (Of which they will be guilty ever)
    Been murderers of so much paper,

Or wasted many a hurtless taper ;
No Indian Drug had e're been famed,
Tobacco, Sassafras not named ;
No yet of Guaiacum one small stick, Sir,
Nor Raymund Lullie's Great Elixir.
Nor had been known the Danish Gonswart,
Or Paracelsus, with his long sword."

" No more Zany," says the doctor, with a wave of his hand.

" Gentlemen, if I had but time to discourse to you the Miraculous effects of this My *Oil*, surnamed *Oglio del Scoto*, with the countless catalogue of those I have cured of the aforesaid and many more diseases, the Patents and Priveleges of all the Princes and Commonwealths of Christendom, or but the Deposition of these that appeared on my part before the Sigmory of the Sanita and most learned College of Physicians, where I was authorised, upon notice taken of the admirable virtues of my medicaments and mine own excellence, in matters of rare and unknown secrets.

" And Gentlemen, honourable Gentlemen, I will undertake by virtue of Chymical Art, out of the honourable hat that covers your head, to extract the four elements, that is to say the Fire, Air, Water and Earth, and return you your Felt without burn or stain !

" Tune your voices once more and give the honourable assembly some delightful recreations."

Zany sings.

" You that would last long, list to my Song,
Make no more coil, but buy of this Oil,

Would you be ever fair and young,
Stout of teeth and strong of tongue,
Tart of palate, quick of ear,
Sharp of sight, of nostril clear,
Moist of hand, and light of foot,
(Nor, I will come nearer to't)
Would you like free from all Diseases,
Do the thing your Mistress pleases,
Yea, fright all aches from your bones,
Here's a med'cine for the Nones."

"Well, Gentlemen, I am in a humour (at this time) to make a present of the small quantity my coffer contains, to the Rich in courtesy and to the Poor for God's sake. Come, you shall not give me the price of six shillings, nor five, nor four, nor three, nor two, nor one. SIXPENCE IT WILL COST YOU, OR SIX HUNDRED POUND.

"Expect no lower price by the Banner of my Front. I will not bate a Bagatine. That, I will have only as a Pledge of your loves to show I am not contemn'd by you.

"Therefore now, toss your handkerchiefs chearfully, and be advertized, that the first heroick spirit that deigns to grace me with a handkerchief, I will give it a little remembrance of something besides shall please it better, than if I had presented it with a double Pistolet.

"Ah, Thank you Lady," Lopus exclaims, as he catches a handkerchief thrown. "I kiss your Bounty, and for this timely grace you have done your poor Scoto, I will return you over and above my Oil, a secret, of that high and inestimable Nature, shall make you for ever enamoured on that minute, wherein your eye first descended on so mean an object.

" Here is a Powder concealed in this paper, of which, if I should speak to the worth, nine thousand volumes were but as one page, that page as a line, that line as a word, so short is this Pilgrimage of man to the expressing of it. I will only tell you, it is the Powder that made Venus a goddess (given her by Apollo) that kept her perpetually young, cleared her wrinkles, firmed her gums, filled her skin, colour'd her hair ; from her derived to Helen and at the sack of Troy (unfortunately) lost till now, in this our age it was as happily recovered by a studious Antiquary out of some Ruins of Asia, who sent a moiety of it to the Court of France, wherewith ladies there now colour their hair ; the rest (at this present) remains with me extracted to a Quintessence, so that wherever it but touches in youth it perpetually preserves, in age restores the complexion, seats your teeth did they dance like virginal Jacks firm as a wall and makes them white as Ivory that were black as H—L."

A bill issued by a " Physician " of the *Blew Ball* in Great-Knight-Rider-street by Doctor's Common announces, that he is privileged to sell the Famous Powder called *Arcanum Magnum* formerly prepared by that Learned Riverius, Physician-Regent to the French King and approved by most persons of Quality in Christendom, for preserving the Face. " Being used in time, it prevents the Face from ever being wrinkled, though they live to a very old age, and it cures all sorts of Red Faces, it takes away all heat pimples, sun-burnt and morphew. (Morphew was the old name for a scurfy skin or that yellowish coloration common to elderly people.)

"It likewise prevents superfluous hair growing on women's faces, and in short, it adds more lustre and beauty to the face, than any other Powder or wash ever prepared by any other person, as many persons of quality in England can testify who do daily use it; and all that use it, do admire it above anything to Beautifie the Face.

"It is prepared by no one in England but at the *Blew Ball*, where it may be had at Twelvepence the Paper, or Two shillings the Paper, that all persons may receive the benefit, though formerly never sold to any but those that would bestow a Guinney at one time of it."

Lazarus Riverius, the famous Italian physician, was the author of several treatises on medicine and pharmacy in the seventeenth century and among them was the "Arcana," which contained the recipe for his *Arcanum Magnum*, said to possess such wonderful properties. This book was translated into English under the title of "The Secrets of the famous Lazarus Riverius" and printed in London in 1685.

From it, there is little doubt, our "Physician of the *Blew Ball*," obtained his prescription. The Arcana or Golden Extract, was composed of Bayberries, Almonds, Elder flowers, Wild grape, Catmint, Wild thyme, Pennyroyal, Carrot seed, Aniseed, Fennell seed, Cummin, Cinnamon, Cloves and Aloes-wood, to which was added Balsam of Peru, with the oils of Nutmeg and Turpentine. These were well mixed and fermented together.

In Petty-France, Westminster, at "a house with a *Black door and a Red Knocker*, between the sign of the *Rose and Crown* and *Jacob's Well*," a German quack established himself, "who hath a Powder which with the blessing of God upon it, certainly cures the Stone and saveth those that have been designed to be cut for it. It wonderfully dissolves Great Stones and brings them away."

This individual appears to be among the first to introduce the so-called stone solvent into London, which later became so much in demand.

The Dutch quacks were almost as numerous in London as the High-German doctors. They doubtless reaped an advantage from the fact, that Holland had a reputation as the seat of medical learning in the seventeenth century, and to the University of Leyden many Englishmen went to study medicine.

"In Crutchet-Fryers near Aldgate, betwixt the *Saracens Head* and the *Kings Arms*, between two Wine-coopers, over against the *Three Golden Anchors*, where you shall see a Hatch at the entry door and a Lanthorn hung over it, dwells that most Renowned Dutch Operator, who lived in the great *City and University of Leyden*.

"He is come over into this most famous Nation at the instances of some persons of quality, that knew in what great credit he lived in Holland, for the cure of men, women, and children.

"He can do such cures, that there is not any example of the like extant, either in books or in the memory of men, for he hath cured even those that had all their guts fallen that could not be thrust back by others, although they had hanged up the poor patient by the feet as if it had been an ox or a calf.

" Now, for to let the world know his Integrity and upright and honest dealing, he maketh this agreement ; that he will not have any money for his pains and medicines, untill half a year after the patient hath been perfectly cured."

Another Dutch quack, who claims Royal patronage, thus announces his arrival. " There is lately arrived in this Kingdom, a *Gentleman* who had the honour to wait upon his Majesty at the General Meeting of the Confederate Princes at the Hague ; who (by reason of an admirable secret which he hath obtained from a Philosopher well-skilled in Natural Causes) had the honour to shew several rare experiments, to the general satisfaction of that gallant and Noble Assembly.

" And now, by the invitation of several persons of Eminence and Quality, does tender for this Kingdom, an *Incomparable Powder*, which at his residence at Rotterdam in Holland, has work'd such wonders and done such notable cures, the like was never yet performed by any medicine in the world.

" He gives it the name Appellation and Title of *Universall*, because there is no Distemper incident to the bodies of mankind, but what it exterpates and utterly eradicates ; and withall, is a medicine so friendly to Nature, that it cures as it were by Sympathy, without any sensible disorder or fateful to the body.

" If the favourable Reader, put but an honourable Construction upon his good intent and meaning, he may in a moment finde that good and benefit which an age can hardly afford him, and since he offers himself to this kingdom as a *Gentleman, not a Physician,* and with this medicine and with no other, the thinking part of mankinde may conclude, that it must of necessity be something not common, and indeed, beyond the reach and capacity of an ordinary pretender.

" It is an easy matter for any person to stile himself a Physician, but to restore bodies decay'd by consumptions, to remove the raging heat of violent Feavours, to restore decaying Nature and prop the trembling frame of weak mortality, and to procure health to all that have been sporting in the Garden of Venus, he never fails to cure, and all with one single medicine.

" This *Universall* and now Incomparable Medicine, I sell for *Six Pound* the ounce and *Three pound* the half ounce.

" You will have no occasion for Apothecaries weights, for with each quantity I sell, I *give a small Silver spoon,* which filled, contains the quantity of a horse-bean that must be taken by the patient.

" My Lodgings are at the *Crown and Jewell* against Exeter Exchange, at a Goldsmith's shop, over against Burley-street, where I am to be spoken with every day from 8 a clock in the morning, till 12 at noon and from 2 till 7 a clock at night."

A Frenchman called Anthony Bellon, who describes himself as a " Doctor of Physick of the University of Montpellier," dwelt at the house of Mr. Edward Stevenson in Bridges-street, just over against the King's Play House, near Covent Garden.

Among his preparations was the *Syrop Vitae* much used at the French Court, which he says is so extraordinary, that "it doth make one live longer and doth preserve Health. He also sells that *Geneva Cordial Water of Lemon*, to which there is no other Liquor to be compared, also a *Coffee powder* to be taken as ordinary coffee with the same taste and smell, but do purge very gently.

"He hath for the ladies all sorts of Waters, perfumed prepared spunges for to clear and smoothen or colour the face. He sels a Lozenge to cure and smoothen Sore lips and also the *Canada Maidenhair Syrop* made with Flowers, and the *Cedar Syrop*."

At the farthest house but one, on the right hand in Deans-court by Deans-street, near St. Ann's church in So-Ho, lived Mr. C. V. P., a Dutch Orthopædic quack, who states, "that he has very good skill, in helping all such whose members of their bodies are out of shape or order ; that is to say, such are inclined to be crooked, having one shoulder or hip higher than the other, or their Legs or Arms anyways distorted. These and any other like irregularities he undertakes by the Blessing of God."

A celebrated High-German Doctor who settled in the Strand, "betwixt St. Clement's Church and Temple Bar, his house being the sign of *The Angel*, just over against Essex-street, and where the pictures of patients and manual operations are over the Door, and WHERE THERE IS A RED CLOTH WITH STONES AND RUPTURES taken out of the patients hanging by," issued an elaborate bill.

It is illustrated with a woodcut worthy of description, representing the interior of an Apothecary's shop, the walls being lined with shelves bearing a great array of jars, pots and bottles. Seated at a table is the doctor receiving his patients, some of whom are cripples hobbling on sticks. The sick visitors are followed by a boy carrying a urine flask for examination. On the left is a large bed draped with curtains and in it a woman is lying. By the bedside is another doctor who is feeling her pulse, and at the foot, a woman is seated in an armchair. In the background, through an archway, a laboratory is depicted with a quantity of retorts, flasks, globe-receivers and other apparatus, together with a still, which is being watched by an assistant.

The bill informs us, that this " Famous High-German Doctor, hath by his great study and constant practice in several parts of the world, as well as in Princes Courts, as in Hospitals and war-like Expeditions, obtained such a physical method as to cure all external and internal Distempers. He can show by Testimonials, not only from Emperors, Kings, Dukes, Electoral Princes, but also from the Right Worshipful Mayor and Alderman of the City of Bristol, Worcester and Hereford, and many other Cities and Corporations in this Kingdom."

He wishes it to be understood, that he is as expert an Oculist as he is excellent in curing the Stone and Rupture, that "the like of him is scarce to be found. He has cured those that were born Blind (by cataract) and restores their sight in *less than a quarter of an hour.*"

The catalogue of diseases he claims to be able to cure is too long to quote in full, it is sufficient to state that it includes " Cancers, crooked legs, and a curious way for curing the King's Evil and an extraordinary method for the treatment of morbus gallicus and many other distempers, which no physicians can give name to."

He also keeps an operator who "cleanses the teeth and makes them white as ivory, extracts aching teeth *with a touch*, fastens loose teeth, and sets in Artificial Teeth as if they were natural."

A
Caveat to the Unwary:

CHAPTER VII

THE QUACK'S COSTUME AND LODGINGS—DR. SALMON
AND SOME OTHERS

THE usual costume of the quack, according to a writer in 1678, consisted of "a decent black suit, and if credit will stretch so far in Long Lane, a plush jacket; not a pin the worse, though threadbare as a taylor's cloak it shows the more reverend antiquity.

"Like Mercury, you must always carry a caduceus or conjuring japan in your hand, capt with a civet-box, with which you must walk with Spanish gravity.

"A convenient lodging, not forgetting a hatch at the door; a chamber hung with Dutch pictures or looking-glasses, belithered with empty bottles, gallipots and vials filled with tar-drippings or fair water coloured with saunders (red sandal wood).

"Any sexton will furnish you with a skull, in hope of your custom, over which hang up the skeleton of a monkey to proclaim your skill in anatomy. Let your table never be without some old musty Greek or Arabick author and the Fourth Book of Cornelius Agrippa's 'Occult Philosophy,' wide open to amuse spectators, also half a dozen of *gilt shillings*, as so many guineas received that morning for fees."

Amidst such surroundings, one can imagine William

Salmon, one of the most notable quack practitioners in London in the seventeenth century, and a man who had an extraordinary career.

He was born on June 2nd 1644, and began life as an assistant to a mountebank with whom he travelled about the country. He then crossed the Atlantic and lived for some time in New England. Returning to London, he first established himself in Smithfield near the gates of St. Bartholomew's Hospital where he treated all who came in his way, sold them medicines and also practised as an astrologer.

His quack remedies, which soon had a considerable sale, included an " Elixir Vitae " or " Elixir of Life," which he claimed to be " a quintessence made of the salts, oyls and spirits of the simples, impregnated with their own proper essences." He also sold the " Family Pills " which acquired a great reputation, and " an antidote against the Plague and all Pestilential Venom, being a specifick against Epidemick Diseases." The latter he states, " certainly takes away and cures melancholy and is without doubt, not only a Restorer of the natural parts but a true and certain prolonger of Life."

He cites in testimony of their virtues the cure of one "Ambrose Webb at the *Three Compasses* in Westbury-street, of a great bleeding at Nose; a youth, a son of William Ogben, a Taylor, near the *Black Boy* in Barnaby-street, of a long and tedious ague and madness; one Cox, who dwelt in Well and Bucket Alley in Old street, of a great obstruction of the liver; Thomas Chew at the *Green man and Still*, a distiller, without Smithfield

Bars, of the Gout ; Nicholas Earl at the *Cup* in Long alley, of dropsie ; Joan Ingram near the *Bear* in Moor Fields of the Gout, and Anthony Geasture at the *Cock* in Wapping of a consumption, together with more than a thousand others."

In spite of his quackery, Salmon was an astute and clever man with considerable literary ability. His enemies declared that he hired some impecunious physician to write certain of his books. In 1671 he published a work entitled " Synopsis Medicinae, or a Compendium of Astrological, Galenical and Chymical Physick," in three books. This was a popular treatise embodying the names of the drugs and chemical substances employed in the medical treatment of his time mixed up with a jumble of astrology and other fantastic theories.

Books of this kind, written in English, at a period when orthodox works on medicine were always printed in Latin, had an attraction for the public, and so the " Synopsis Medicinae " met with success and passed through four editions.

Salmon did not confine his literary efforts to medicine alone, as in 1672, he published a book called " Polygraphica, or the Art of Drawing, Engraving, Etching, Limning, Painting, Washing, Varnishing, Colouring and Dyeing," which he dedicated to Peter Stanley of Alderley, who appears to have consulted him on matters of art. This work shows that he had some knowledge of the graphic arts and in it he describes various methods of representing the passions and emotions in portraiture. This also proved successful and it ran into eight editions.

He removed from Smithfield to the " Red Balls " in Salisbury Court off Fleet Street, and from this address, published his " Horae Mathematicae " in 1679, the " Iatrica seu Praxis Medendi " in 1681, and " Doron Medicon " in 1683.

In 1684, he again removed to the " Blue Balcony by the ditch side near Holbourne Bridge." It was here in 1684 he first published his " London Almanack " afterwards called " Salmon's Almanack " which combined prophecies with dates and was a precursor of Old Moore.

In 1689, he ventured into anatomy and with Edward Brewster published a translation of the " Anatomy " of Diemerbrock, the famous surgeon of Utrecht. This was followed by two more popular works on medicine viz., "The Family Dictionary or Household Companion" in 1696, and " Seplasium, the complete English Physician or the Druggists Shop opened," in 1693.

From the " Blue Balls " in Mitre court in Fleet street, he again began to issue bills advertising his " Family Pills," which he recommends for innumerable diseases; his " Cordial Drops " to comfort the heart in old or young, and his " Balsam " for all pains, sprains and swellings. " Many bedridden," he says, " and given over to all appearance, have unexpectedly met with a cure, almost to a miracle, in so much, that many learned Phisitians could not but admire at their virtues."

Like other quacks he developed strong religious views and carried them to a fanatical extent. He became a prominent member of a sect called the "New Religious Fraternity of Free-thinkers " that met near Leather-

seller's Hall, where he was wont to expound his theological doctrines.

On account of this, in 1700, he was attacked in an
amusing broad-side entitled, " The Religious Impostor
or the Life of Alexander——A sham prophet, doctor and
fortune-teller, by Sebastian Smith Esq.   Printed in
Amsterdam, for the Company of the Saints of the
New Stamp, in the first year of grace and free-thinking,
and sold next door to the Devil."

It is dedicated " to the Worthy Doctor S-lm-n and
the Company of the Saints of the New Impression alias
the Free-thinkers," and purports to give an account of
Salmon's early life and career.

The author alludes to him as Alexander, and declares
that when a boy he was apprenticed to a mountebank
whom he served as a " Whachum or Zany, and used to
inveigle and direct the amazed silly Rout, with tumb-
ling through a hoop and vaulting and amusing 'em with
tricks of legerdemain and sleight of hand.   He served
him also as Jugler, Sub-conjurer, astrologer, ganymede
and orator ;   made speeches and wrote Panegyricks in
praise of his master's Panaceas. He wrote Almanacks to
direct the taking of his medicines and made the stars
vouch for their virtues.   He calculated Nativities, told
fortunes, had admirable Secrets to Soddercrack'd
maidenheads, and Incomparable Philtres for the con-
solation of Dispairing Damsels.

" He succeeded to his Quack-master's business and
on his travels met with a man, part-author and part-
book-seller, who had an excellent knack of canting and
counterfeiting religion, and to him imparted his design

of setting up as a prophet and they became partners in the strategem. It is easy to apprehend for what I give you this summary of the History of Alexander, whom I take to have been a type of you," the biographer says in conclusion.

" The Churchyards and Burying places are everywhere ample witnesses of your travels. You teach when to cut corns and let blood. By you, old Nurses are instructed to make Carduus-Possets and Chalybeate Pancakes, bawds to cause abortions and strumpets to counterfeit maidenheads. In a word, Pious Sir, may you never cease to hold the sucking-bottle of the gospel to the babes of grace, and the crutches of faith to the crippled Saint."

Salmon next became involved in theological discussions and in 1690, published " A Discourse against Trans-substantiation," in the form of a dialogue between " a Protestant and a Papist."

Incensed at Sir Samuel Garth's allusion to him as a " Quack-Astrologer " in his poem " The Dispensary," which caused a great deal of controversy at the time, he wrote a reply entitled, " Rebuke to the Authors of a Blew Book, written on behalf of the Apothecaries and chirurgians of the City of London."

In 1692 he published his " Medicina Practica or the Practical Physician," and his last two works, which show his versatility, were the " English Herbal or a History of Plants" in 1710, and " Ars Anatomica or the Anatomy of the Humane Bodie" in 1714. These however do not by any means exhaust the list of his publications, which are recorded in Bibliotheca Salmonca, printed in

London in 1713. Salmon made a considerable sum of money by the sale of his nostrums and books. He formed a large library and was the possessor of two microscopes, several mathematical instruments and many interesting curiosities which he had gathered during his travels abroad. After his death, a catalogue of part of his library was published by Thomas Ballard, Bookseller, at "The Rising Sun" in Little Britain, and they were sold by auction at St. Paul's Coffee-house on November 16th 1713.

Ballard, in a preface, comments on William Salmon's extraordinary love of books and his singular judgment in the choice of them. He had over 3,000 volumes, and a glance at their titles show they included most of the works on Physic and Surgery printed in the XVIIth century, rare copies of the Classics, many Bibles, a very complete library of contemporary medicine and a good proportion of works on Mathematics, Theology, Botany and Alchemy printed in the XVIth century.

Mrs. Salmon carried on what was probably the first wax-work show in London at the Turkish Seraglio in St. Martins near Aldersgate Street, in the early days of Queen Anne's reign.

She combined the art of modelling wax figures with that of making glass eyes. In her bill she states that, " She takes likenesses of Gentlemen and Ladies and has on view the Temple of Ephesus, of Apollo, the Vision of Augustus and the Six Sybyls, moving figures. Also an old woman flying from time who shakes his head and hour-glass with sorrow at seeing age so unwilling to die. Nothing but life can exceed the motions of the heads, hands, eyes of these figures." Mrs. Salmon, who claims to teach the full art, removed soon afterward from St. Martin's-le-grand to the "Golden Salmon" at Temple Bar which, she says, "is a more convenient place for the coaches of the quality to stand unmolested."

A curious case of a Licentiate of the College of Physicians who turned Quack-doctor, is that of John Pechey, who was born in 1654 and at the age of seventeen, matriculated at Oxford as a member of New Inn Hall and graduated as Master of Arts in 1678.

Returning to Chichester, where his father practised as a physician, he probably learned from him the rudiments of medicine, for in the year 1684, he took up his residence in London and applied for a licence to practice. At this time, three examinations were necessary to become a licentiate of the College of Physicians, the first being in Physiology, the rudiments of medicine with questions on Anatomy; the second in Pathology, and the third on the use and exercise of medicine.

Although he failed at first to satisfy the Examiners, he obtained the licence at the end of 1684 and went to live at Chequer Yard near Dowgate. He was the translator of the first English version of the works of Sydenham and published several other works on medicine. In 1687, together with two colleagues, he obtained the lease of the *Golden Angel and Crown* in King Street, Cheapside, and there established a Dispensary, concerning which he issued a bill to the public.

In this, he gives his rules for patients, which were as follows :

" 1. A certain time shall be agreed upon for the cure of the diseases before they are undertaken.

" 2. The sick shall know first what the medicines will cost that are necessary for their cure, tho' they shall pay for them only as they use them.

" 3. Whatever is received for medicines of them shall be faithfully return'd, if the case be not perfected within the time prefixt.

" 4. That they may be sure of either having their money or their health restored ; they or their friends for them, shall have a note, if they desire it, under my hand and seal, for the performance of these proposals.

" I will visit them in any part of the City of London in the day time for two shillings and sixpence, and will ride to visit patients in the City of Westminster or in Southwark or the Suburbs, for two and sixpence a mile ; the messenger that comes for me, leaving the said fee at my house, and the name of the person that sends for me and of the place of his or her abode."

Pechey's propensity for issuing bills and advertising, soon brought him into trouble with the College, and we find in November 1688, he was summoned to appear before the Censors " upon printing bills " and was admonished ; but he still continued, with the result, he was brought before the College again and again and fined several times, all of which he refused to pay.

As an excuse for his unprofessional conduct, Pechey then issued a bill stating, " Many ill men make it their business to reproach this publick way of practice, because it thwarts their interest, but undoubtedly all persons that are free from prejudice, will approve of it."

" At the *Angel and Crown* in Basing Lane, being the second turning in Bread Street from Cheapside, there lives John Pechey of long-standing in the Colledge of Physicians in London, and because it is commonly reported that Physicians will do nothing without their fees, he proposes to undertake certain diseases including Deafness, Sore-eyes, Coughs, Consumptions, Stomack-pains, Jaundice, Fevers and Agues for nothing till the cure is performed."

In 1693, he advertises that " The sick may have advice for nothing and excellent Purging Pills prepared by J. Pechey of the College of Physicians ; My Elixir for the Stone and Chollick, price 2s. 6d., and other approved medicines for the cure of other diseases."

In another bill, in which he describes himself as " a Graduate in the University of Oxford," he states, " all sick People that come to him may have for sixpence a faithful account of their diseases, and Plain Directions for diet and other things, they can prepare themselves." He further gives a description of his ten secret remedies including his Worm Powders at 4d. each.

Meanwhile, further trouble developed with the College on account of his refusal to pay his yearly payment of 40/- due by the Statute, and for this they entered an action against him which was tried at the Guildhall.

When the Beadle called upon him afterwards to demand his money and threatened more drastic measures, Pechey told him, " to bid the College begin when they pleased." Whereupon the Board ordered him to be

arrested and prosecuted according to law! Apparently
this was not carried out, for in 1706 he removed from
the *Angel and Crown* to Bow Lane, where he resided
until his death in 1718.

The quack of to-day, who advertises his nostrum by
offering to send the recipe for it to any anxious inquirer,
is but imitating some of his predecessors, who carried on
the same business three hundred years ago. In this way
Mr. Joseph Sabbarton of *The Bleeding Pelican*, exploited
his " True Compound Elixir of Scurvy-grass and
Horse-radish."

According to his bill, in order to make it, you are to
" take Horse-radish roots 10 pounds, Scurvy-grass
seeds 8 pounds, Sea and garden Scurvy-grass of each
10 pounds, Winters Lignamon 4 pounds. Bruise the
seeds, reduce the bark to powder, macerate the herbs in a
marble mortar, then extract an Elixir according to the
SPAGERICK ART.

" But, if you want it RIGHTLY PREPARED you
must seek Mr. Sabbarton at the Norwich Coffee-house in
Dean's Court in St. Martin's-le-Grand, near Aldersgate,
where he sells it at one shilling per glass, *sealed with the
Bleeding Pelican.*"

" Every Man his own Doctor," is the title of a pamphlet published by J. A. One of his Majesty's Physicians
to advertise his remedies. " This Doctor is to be spoke
with and gives advice from 2 till night at his chamber
at the Haymarket by Charing Cross, next the *White
Horse Inne*, a *Strong-Water-Shop* where his medicines
are to be had." In the long list which follows, these
preparations include his *Elixir Proprietatis* sold at 5s.

an ounce, *Elixir Guiaci*, *Aqua Cordialis*, his *prepared Tobacco* for dropsie, his *Sneeze Powder* for convulsions and falling sickness, his *Cordial Diet Drink*, his *Morbus Pills*, his *Stichback Pills* and *Purging Bolus* at 3s. 6d. the pot.

" If you think the quantities mentioned are too great, they may be had for one shilling, of any sort," he naïvely remarks in conclusion.

His " Pectoral Lozenges as your companions by day and his Balsamick Syrup as your guard by night," is the appeal of Edward Andrews M.D. who lived at the second house on the right hand in Bolt and Tun Yard, in Fleet-street. " These are the two greatest remedies extant for the Restauration and Preservation of the Lungs, Breast and Organs of Respiration. The *Gemelli Pulmonales* or Pectoral Lozenges and *Balsamick Syrup* you must know, do joyntly and mutually operate with Admirable effect in the Cure of the various Distempers of those Noble Parts."

Dr. Andrews also issued a broadside, which he called *Panoplia Medica* or a Medicinal Armour for the whole Body, in which he claims " to give proof against the Invasion of sickness and Assault of Destroying Diseases. Being composed of the greatest *Arcana* and select medicines in the whole Practical Part of Physick."

The *Arcana* consisted of " Our Great Stomach Pills whose primary intentions are the Relief and support of that Noble Part.

" The next is our *Grand Antiscorbutick* call'd *Anima Cochleariae* or the Soul of Scurvy-grass, next our *Pulmoniack Lozenges* and last our *Alexiterial Balsamick*

Syrup for the Lungs and Breathing Organs.   A fourth medicine.   The *Tincture of Mars* or *Steel,* a Medicine indeed ! which never till now, made its publick entry, that I never mett with or heard of any that exceeded it.

" To which I beseech God to give his blessing."

CHAPTER VIII

A QUACK-DOCTOR AND BALLAD-SINGER—A HIGH GERMAN DOCTOR AND HIS MERRY ANDREW

AN extraordinary character, well-known in the district round St. Giles, the Seven Dials and Smithfield towards the end of the XVIIth century, was Jack Edwards.

Every one in the neighbourhood knew Jack as a merry fellow, ever ready with a quip or to crack a joke with passers-by, for he practically lived in the streets. He combined the callings of Quack-doctor, Ballad-singer and Merry Andrew, but was particularly successful in treating horses for various disorders.

When trade, in selling his medicines in the markets and at street corners, fell off, he would turn Zany to some fellow practitioner, sing ballads, or distribute bills, and afterwards return to his mountebank pranks and sell his own pills and potions.

His demise was commemorated by an " Elegy on the much *unlamented* death of John Edwards—The Horse-Doctor and Merry Andrew," which was sold as a broadside about the streets and from which the following is extracted :

" Alas, what sudden news flies o'er the Town,
In one we've lost a Gentleman and a Clown,
Jack Edwards, thro' the sudden want of Breath,
Is gone to play Jack Dindle's part with Death.

* * * * * *

T' oblige the mobb that did some Pastime lack,
He'd Merry Andrew turn ; and name of Quack
Forsake a Fortnight, then that time expired
The name of Doctor was again acquired.
His horse and he for nothing gave advice,
Nay sware if any took his Pills but thrice.
If Blind he'd so restore you to your sight
That you should never more perceive the Light,
If Deaf, such practice try upon your Ear
That Drum nor Cannon you should never hear ;
But now, poor Jack's as any herring Dead,
And will no more dull people cheat for bread.
This Quack and Merry Andrew for the D—l
When living to the mobb was very civel,
For if his antick tricks their Coyn could get,
He'd give them leave to laugh at his dull Wit.
Death fell a laughing at this vain discourse
And told poor Edwards, who was very hoarse.
'Twas now, just now, that we did lack,
An Andrew, Ballad-singer and a Quack.
So giving Jack a dose which made him stare,
He sent him headlong straight, the Lord knows
     where ;
Too sure our Mountebank is gone to sleep,
So all you simple people sadly weep,

Who've often stood to hear him Nonsense prate,
And bought the Drugs he sold about the Street.

Epitaph

" Here lies a Songster, Fool and Quack,
But which of all these three,
He really had the chiefest knack
Is nought to you and me,
But see the Fool whose noisome Drugs
Has stopt some People's breath,
For all his skill could not secure
Himself from greedy Death."

" Jack Edwards departed this life, on Saturday the 16th of this instant November, at his Seat in Castle-street in the Parish of St. Giles-in-the-Fields in 1706."

The Zany often played an important part on the stage and sometimes introduced his master to the audience (when he happened to be a foreigner) in a mock-speech, of which the following is an example :

" Gentlemen. Tho' I am an English Fool yet my Master has the Honour to be a High-German Physician, who in his travels round the Universe, has cured twelve Foreign Ministers of State of those Twin Plagues, Bribery and Infidelity ; six kinds of a Tyranical Fevers, the whole Conclave of Cardinals of Pride, Laziness and Hypocrisy and the present Pope of the Anti-Christian Evil !

" He was also three years Oculist to the German Spread-Eagle, and Seven years Operator for the Teeth to the King of Spain's White Elephants. He is not only Learn'd by his Studies, but Reverend as you may see by his Beard, and Wise, as you may judge by his silence.

"He has made himself by his long travels master of all the Tongues in the whole World.

"Amongst the many excellent medicaments contain'd in his little Health-preserving packet, the first thing that he presents with is this minute Panopharmacon which he calls his 'Infallible Pill,' tho' 'tis so small in bulk that it is scarce discernable without a microscope, yet is so mighty in its operation, that it will raise the weakest patient out of his sick-bed and make him strong enough in two minutes to encounter Conscience, Death and the Devil.

"In the next place, he communicates to your view his most excellent umbellical 'Sticking Plaister,' which if applied by the wife to the pit of her husband's stomack, disperses all manner of jealous Heart-burnings, prevents the many violent Evils that daily arise from that predominant, Monarchical Distemper, such as grumbling in the Gizard, Murder, Imprisonment and the like; these, with all its evil concomitants it disperses in a moment and so strengthens his appetite towards family duty, that he will be able to love wonderfully and beget a miraculous progency.

"Lastly, to crown the whole number of his Admirable secrets, here is that rich and excellent Preservative, as well as antidote, his ORVIETANO. Take but a small dose of this next your heart in a morning, and you may venture anytime of the day after into the most disaffected Coffee-house in London, without the danger of being poisoned with Rebellious Principles. It expels all Low-Country Schism, carries off all Disloyalty, and is the best restorative to strengthen weak Faith and decay'd Allegiance, that ever was yet discover'd since the fall of Adam. And all these Medicines, contain'd in this little Packet, the Doctor, through his Bounty to the Publick, is willing to let you have for the small value of sixpence."

Here follows the speech of a High-German Doctor, who apparently had a remarkable command of the English language.

" I am a High-German Doctor who, by the blessing of Aesculapius on his great Pains, Travels and Nocturnal Lucubrations, has attained to a greater share of knowledge than any person before him was ever known to do.

" IMPROMIS. Gentlemen, I present you with my ' Universal Solutive ' which corrects all the Cacochymick and Cachexical Diseases of the Intestines, Hydrocephalous, Epileptick Fits, Flowing of the Gall and many other distempers not hitherto distinguished by name.

" Secondly. My ' Friendly Pills ' call'd the Never Failing Heliogenes, which work by dilating and expanding the Gelastick Muscles, first of all discovered by myself.

" They clear the Officina Intelligentiæ, correct the Exorbitancy of the Spleen, mundify the Hypogastrium, comfort the Sphincter and are an excellent remedy against Prosopo Chlorosis or Green sickness.

" They operate seven several ways viz. Hypnotically, Hydrotically, Cathartically, Proppysinatically, Hydragogically, Pulmatically, and lastly Synecdochically, by corroborating the whole Oeconomia Animalis.

"There are twenty or more in every Tin box, sealed with my Coat of arms, which are Three glyster-pipes erect Gules in a field Argent, and my crest is a bloody hand out of a Mortar emergent, and my supporters, a Chymist and an Apothecary.

"This 'Tincture Solaris' or Most Noble Offspring of Hyperious Golden Influence, wipes off abstertively all those tenacious, sedimental sordes that adhere to the Oesophagus and Viscera, and annihilates all the noso-trophical Ideas of the whole Corporeal.

"Thirdly. My 'Panagion Outaconsticon' or Auri-cular Restorative, were it possible to shew me a man so deaf, that if a Demiculverin were to be let off under his ear, he could not hear the report, yet these infallible Drops (first invented by the two Famous Physicians and Brothers, St. Cosmas and St. Damian) and some forty years ago communicated to me by Anastasio Logotheti, a Greek Colyr at Adrianople, when I was invited to those parts to cure Sultan Mahomet IV of Elephantiasis in his Diaphragm, he would recover his auditive faculty and hear as smartly as any old fumbling priest when a young wench gives him her confession.

"Lastly, my 'Pulvis Vermifugus' or Ante-vermick Powder, so famous for killing and bringing away all sorts of worms incident to human bodies. It has brought away Worms as long as the Maypole in the Strand when it flourished in its primitive prelixity, though I confess not altogether so thick.

"I dexterously couch the cataract, extirpate Wens of

the greatest magnitude, close up Hair-Lips, likewise take the Stone from all Women or Maids without cutting.

" I forge all myself, nay my very machines, for safe and easy drawing Teeth and obscure stumps.

" Mrs. Littlehand, midwife to the Princes of Phlegethon, can sufficiently inform the women of my Helps, and if any woman be unwilling to speak to me, they may have the conveniency of speaking to my wife who is expert in all feminine distempers. She has an excellent Cosmetick Water to carry off Freckles, Sunburn or Pimples and a curious Red Pomatum to plump and colour the lips, while she can make Red Hair as white as a Lilly. Also a rare secret that takes away all warts from the face, hands, fingers and other parts.

" I have predicted miraculous things by the Pulse, far above any Philosopher. By it, I not only discover the circumstances of the body, but if the party be a woman, I can fortel how many Husbands and Children she shall have ; if a Tradesman, whether his wife will fortify his forehead with Horns and so of the rest.

" By my learning and great travels I have obtained the true and perfect seed and blossom of the Female Fern, and infinately improved that great traveller, Major John Choke's famous Necklace for breeding the teeth.

" My hours are from 9 till 12 and from 2 till 9, every day in the week, except on the real CHRISTIAN SABBATH CALLED SATURDAY."

CHAPTER IX

QUACK-doctoring was by no means confined to the male sex in the seventeenth century, and the female of the species, who preyed chiefly on members of her own sex, flourished in old London.

She usually introduces herself as a "Gentlewoman," but occasionally she is the "wife of a famous doctor now deceased."

In the year 1693, we learn from a bill, that Mrs. Mary Green living at a *Haberdasher of Hats*, next door to the *Three Crane Tavern*, in Chancery-lane, "hath, by the Blessing of God and many years practice, learned a most Excellent Method of Curing those Distempers which shall be later mentioned."

Mrs. Mary Green, be it known, is "Licensed by His Grace, the Lord Archbishop of Canterbury, for the great cures she hath performed on Several Persons ; the truth of which you may be satisfied by repairing to her House in Chancery-lane.

"She cures all Deadness, Numbness, Weakness of Limbs, Rheumatisms, and Sciaticas, tho' of many years standing. Many of them should have had their Arms and Leggs cut off by the advice of many eminent Doctors in and about London.

"Mr. Robert Smith, who two years ago was struck by a *Planet* on his left Arm, and did then apply himself to the ablest Physicians and Chirurgeons in London and found no relief, but applying himself to the said Mrs. Green was in a short time perfectly cured by her, and is now as well as any man can be.

"Also Mrs. Atkins, a Midwife in Scroop's Court against St. Andrew's Church, Holbourn, was lame in all her limbs, did for Five years consult the Ablest Doctors and likewise THE WHOLE COLLEDGE OF PHYSICIANS, was perfectly cured by Mary Green. She hath also cured Mrs. Dixter in Hanging-Sword Alley in Fleet Street, and Mr. Vaughan, Clark to the White-Lyon-Wharf near Barnard's Castle in Thames street, who was troubled with the Ptisck (chest trouble) and Mrs. Batler, over against the *Pewter Platters* in St. John's street, who had a White swelling of which she was perfectly cured by me."

The "Gentlewoman" sometimes combined the sale of cosmetics and other aids to the toilet with the practice of medicine. Thus, "Be it known, that in St. Martin's Court in St. Martin's lane, at the sign of the *Golden Heart*, up one pair of stairs, Liveth a Gentlewoman who by the long experience of her predecessors, as likewise from her own practice for several years past, hath attained to great knowledge in things relating to the Female sex, which she is unwilling to conceal, knowing them far to exceed anything exposed by the Common Pretenders of the Town. Therefore, she is persuaded by several Persons of Quality, to make this general Publication.

"First. She hath a most incomparable Wash to beautifie the Face, agreeable to all manner of Complexions, which takes off pimples, freckles, morphew or what else may obstruct a fair and lovely complexion. It leaves such an agreeable Lustre, that the most Curious Eye cannot perceive art to be used, but will judge it to be the true product of Nature.

" Second.   She hath also a most Delicate Pomatum, which is wonderfully agreeable to be used with it.   A Summer's day is too short to demonstrate the full virtues of both these, therefore for brevity's sake she omits it.

" Third.   She hath Red and White Handkerchiefs (these were used for colouring or whitening the skin as required).

" Fourth.   She hath a fine Lip-Salve.

" Fifth.   She hath all sorts of delicate Pearl Powders to whiten the skin.

" Sixth.   She hath most curious Masks and Forehead cloths, which take out all spots, pits, scars, caused by the small-pox, and also all wrinkles of the face."

The masks and cloths for application to the face, were usually made of coarse linen which had been dipped in a hot mixture of wax, gum benzoin and oil.   In earlier times they were sometimes called cere-cloths.

Besides the preparations mentioned, this " gentlewoman " had a Rare Dentifrice Powder and Water for the Teeth to make them white as Ivory.   " She shapeth the Eye-brows, and also hath a great Secret to prevent Hair falling and causing it to grow where it is wanting. She hath a fine ointment to anoint the face so soon as the Small-pox begins to dry, and a Goldon Unction te cure all old ulcers in the leggs, altho' of never so many years standing."

The disfigurement caused by small-pox which was so prevalent in England at this period, marred the beauty of many women, a fact commented on by several contemporary writers.

"In Holbourn over and against Southampton-square at the sign of *The Coffin and Child*, against the *Watch-house*, next door to the *Sugar-Loaf and Role*, where a *Golden Ball* hangeth over the passage door, liveth Anne Laverenst, a German Gentlewoman."

Anne informs the public, that she has but very lately arrived in this Kingdom, and so is consequently a stranger, it behoves her therefore to make herself known by a printed paper, otherwise she might for some years remain *un*known.   She says that her parents before her, were so far skilled in the art and knowledge of physick, that "they have removed the most dangerous dis-tempers and have seldom or never failed wholesomely to assist Nature in the discharge of her duty."   From them she received the great knowledge and experience that she now professes, and questions not, but (by the blessing of God) she will be able to cure any distemper incident to woman-kind.

Following a long list of ailments to which her sex are susceptible, Anne states, that she also cures the Morbus Gallicus and presumes few have arrived to the perfection in this cure than herself.   She offers to those who require close confinement to their chambers, lodging at her house and accommodation, with all things necessary at a reasonable rate.

In a later bill headed with a device of the double eagle and the words *cum Privilegio*, addressed to "Ladies and all others of the Female Sex" she announces, that she now lives in Arundel street, over against the *King's Arm's Tavern*, near St. Clement's Church in the Strand, "where you will see a *RED CLOTH hang out at the Balcony, with coagulated stones taken out of the bodies of the Female Sex*," a gruesome sign indeed for a Gentlewoman practising chirurgery.

At the Sign of *The Garden of Eden* in the Old Bailey, next Ludgate-hill, lived a Gentlewoman "who after twenty years experience cures all sorts of scal'd Heads and leprosies without the least pain, and hath performed great cures in old and young. She desires nothing for her pains till she hath performed the Cure."

The wives and daughters of the quacks sometimes carried on or took an active part in their practice, and among them was "The Doctor's Wife" of Dean's Court, who was famous for the cure of all Female Distempers.

In a bill addressed specially "to Ladies, Gentlewomen and Others," she states, that having left off for some time, for the sake of her health, now through God's blessing, she is enabled to lend her best help to those of her sex. She claims to have had almost Thirty years Experience and Practise at Home and Abroad, in Germany, Spain, France and other parts of Europe, where she hath attained to the knowledge of the most Rare and most Effective Remedies. She hath made it her chief business and study during her various long travels, to attain to the knowledge of the Best, Rarest and most Wonderful Secrets which Art and Nature can afford for the cure of Barrenness.

" To those whom God hath made so, none can make Fruitful, but so far as anything can be done by Art, she will undertake by God's blessing to do it, insomuch, that if a Woman should be 20, nay 25 years married, she may hope to be Bless'd ; as great numbers of Women, many of them of Quality, have experienced and will testify.

" She still lives in Dean's Court, in St. Martin's-le-Grand, near Aldersgate, at the sign of *The Hand and Urinal*, and is to be spoken with at any reasonable hours."

The Widow Drew, who was the daughter of a " Doctor of Physick and who for twenty years and upwards visited her Father's patients, prepared physick for them and administered to all her sex," announces, that "since her father's decease, to improve herself she has lived with Dr. Rose, the Man-Midwife. Her Pills certainly cure the green-sickness and change the pale, greenish Tallow coloured, nasty and Death-like look of the patient, into a fair, lovely, florid and healthy complexion.

" Many hundreds of young Virgins have had the benefit of these pills, which may be had at the sign of the *Blue Ball*, at the upper end of Gun-Yard in Houndsditch, near Aldgate."

The Widow Drew apparently combined the calling of draper with that of the quack, for she adds, " At the same house likewise are sold all sorts of childrens coats, by wholesale or retail."

Agnodice, the Woman Physician, who lived at the *Hand and Urinal* next door to the *Blue Ball* in Hayden Yard in the Minories, near Aldgate, claimed to have special abilities as a healer and maker of preparations for the complexion.

She recommends a " Tincture for fits, a Powder for the green-sickness, a Pill for a dry cough, a Diet-Drink to cure the King's Evil, an Infusion for a ' third day '— Ague, Pillets and Pouder to Purge the Head, a Water for Sore-Eyes, an Elixir for Gravel and many other remedies too tedious to mention."

She states " to her own Sects, she cures all diseases or accidents that may or can attend them, although given over by others as is daily experienced. *The diseases in particular I shall forbear to mention, they being not proper to be exposed to the Publick.*

" If Venus should misfortunately be wounded with a Scorponious Poyson by tampering with Fiery Mars, to her own Sects it is then she brings comfort and relief, and by her antidotes expels the poyson, Jove-like, though never so far gone."

She also mentions that she cures very speedily the *Scotch Disease*, a name which in former times was applied to the itch.

Owing to her travels for many years in foreign parts, from which she has brought back ever such curiosities as was never published or known in England before, Agnodice claims to have some wonderful preparations for the skin. These include her " Italian Wash, which takes away all cutaneous effects and blemishes in the skin, making the face most clear and Fair. The "Spanish

Rolls," a little being scraped into Fair water takes away wrinkles and pits of Small-pox and makes the hands and face smooth, white and lovely.

"She hath also a Liquid which adds to the Face a fresh and Lively lustre and Colour, proper for all those that look as pale as death.

"Her excellent pomatums doth work wonders and have a rare art in shaping the Eyebrows, making low fore-heads high, making the hair grow thicker and colouring it what they please.

"These," she concludes, "are Remedies daily experienced by Persons of Great Quality, who have and do commend them to all their acquaintances."

A Madam Gordan of Goodman's Fields adopted a curious method of advertising her medicines. In her bill dated 1695, which she heads, "By His Majesty's Authority," she announces that she has "Two Monsters on view, which by medicines prescribed by her to Robert Cobb, a labourer who lives in White-Horse Ally in Barbican, who had been Labouring under an unknown Distemper for several years ; and after being given over by many Physitians, was, by her medicines and God's assistance, delivered of one Monster the 9th of October 1695, *like a Lyon* ; and of one other the 5th of June 1696, *like a Fox*, both of which he vomited up at his mouth and are now to been seen. VIVAT REX."

Sarah Cornelius de Heusde, "widow of Dr. Sasbout, and grandmother of the Doctor that had his stage upon Great Tower Hill and did so many cures before the Fire," issued a bill, that was "To be delivered into the

Hands of Civil Gentlewomen and Maidens," which begins thus :

" Loving Reader,

" God Almighty hath not created man for himself, neither for his own ends, but hath given him natural affection for to Love his Fellowes and loving them to cure them by all means, and whereas I have many Sciences and Mysteries of Nature, likewise particular experiences, new inventions, natural secret arts to cure many and divers great and dangerous accidents, as well internal as external, specially for women and young maidens.

" It may be, some will say, that this my Science is but a deceitful enterprize, as there are some old women and midwives who sometimes have a little book out of which they gather their sciences.

" But it is not so with me, who have learned these my sciences of my Father and Husband, who both were physicians and of such esteem amongst men, as well noble, as others, that there appeared no accidents however so great in the humane body, as well men as women, whereunto their advice had not been required."

Sarah then gives a long list of the diseases in which she has been successful, and among them, that curious distemper, " incident to young maidens who long to eat strange things like morter, stone, sand and coals.

" Those also who are troubled with *heavy thoughts*, that they were in a rage or mad, so that they endeavoured to kill themselves or another.

" I further make a Beautifying for the Body, as well

for Fair Colours for the Face, as for the Hands, *without painting*. I make the hair to fall out when it is too thick, and make it grow where it is too little, and can colour it according to everyone's fancy.

" Therefore, if there be any person who hath occasion for this famous Operatoress, she liveth at the sign of *The Red Lyon*, by the postern Gate in George Yard, between Great and Little Tower Hill, where she is to be spoken withall, between 8 in the morning and 8 in the evening."

The Virtues of that " Famous Friendly Pill, Electuary and Balsam of Balsams," invented by the late Dr. George Jones of Hatton Garden are extolled in a bill issued by Elizabeth Russell "that was Dr. Jones' Widdow, but who is now married again and lives at the *Two Blew Posts*, against Grayes-Inn in Holbourn.

" The Friendly Pills, being the Tincture of the Sun, having dominion from the same light, giving Relief and Comfort to all mankind are a wonder among other wonderful medicines.

" They cause all complexions to laugh or smile in the very time of taking them. They are Twenty or more in every Tin box sealed with the *Lyon and Cinquefoil*, and the price one shilling.

" They are as big as pins heads and very easie to be taken. Take all the Twenty, or *so many as you find in the box, all at once*, last going to bed and sleep on them, and if you find the first taking hath not finished the cure, continue taking *another box* every second or third night or till you are well."

The list of diseases they will cure is too lengthy to be

quoted here, but it is sufficient to state that " they extinguish all supernatural Ferments, and Destroy the Disasiefying Idaea of the whole Body."

Some of the accounts given by Elizabeth of her cures, however, may be worth mentioning. " The Electuary," she states, " Cured the wife of Mr. Randal at Deptford, *almost blind* with the King's Evil, and took a Worm *four yards* long from Mr. Colbrook, against the Old Hole-in-the-Wall in Baldwin's garden by Holbourn. Other cures lately done, are on January 17th 1678, John Tichberry, a Cooper, on the Bank-side in Southwark near Marygold stairs, after taking two boxes of pills, voided *a Stone*. Henry Butterfield at Wemly in Harrow Parish, was cured of a surfit and Feaver ; Mrs. Field living at Harrow-upon-the-Hill, sorely afflicted with great pain in her limbs, was cured by a few boxes of these pills.

" They also cured Mr. John Davis of Pickle-herring-stairs, at *The Five Tobacco Pipes*, of the Ague ; Lettis Story, who had the Evil in her mouth ; the pills and balsam cured her and she continues well ; George Stone of Arsal parish in Surrey, whose body was swolled so big, that his cloathes would not come together by a foot, took 6 boxes and he was cured. Likewise Mr. Edward Mallord in Hare-street, at the sign of *The Mallet and Tobacco-roul*, in Stepney parish, was cured of the Scurvy when he was *broken out in knobs*, and the child of Mr. Hugh Gardiner, a barber in Milk street, at the sign of *The Hand and Perriwig*, near the Market, was cured of a violent Fever."

A " Gentlewoman who lives at the *Blew Ball* in

little Kerby street in Hatton Garden, in Holbourn, who without making any preamble as to how or from whence she gained her Art, is willing to tell the world in a few words that (through the blessing of God) she is to a wonder, successful in working a speedy cure on those that have either Rickets or Deafness.

" She hath a Sear-cloath which hath been highly approved by several for taking away all manner of Pains and Aches."

This " Gentlewoman hath likewise a most Excellent and Wonderful art to make the hair grow wherever it be wanting, *though there had been none before.* She also hath a Water that takes all sorts of *worms* out of the face, and is always ready to give an answer to any reasonable question that shall be askt her of what kind soever it be, whether of things past, things now depending, or things to come."

Among the women quacks who claimed to cure the "Stone" was Mrs. Norridge, who states that her father, Dr. Duncan, left her a *great Secret* on his decease, for an " Infallible powder " to dissolve the Stone.

This Powder, she says, " hath been several times in the *Gazette* for the general good of mankind and you may confirm the truth about it, to those that are either envious or unbelieving, of the Vise-Countess Lamsbury at her House over against Mr. Notts, the Stationer in Pall-Mall, of Mr. Guilbart, Knight of the Shire for Darbyshire and his Lady, both experienc'd it, and Alice Fielding servant to the Countess of Kingston.

" She hath also a useful Powder, that takes away the sharp humour of the blood which causes violent itching, so that many persons are forced to *scratch so much* it makes them like *Leopards.*

" She hath likewise the greatest secret in the world for Deafness, which was left to her by her father, who cured the deaf and dumb from their birth, and others that had been deaf for the space of Twenty years and could neither hear *Drum* or *Trumpet.*

" She setteth Artificial Teeth and cureth toothache immediately.

" Her excellent Water for Sore-Eyes cured Mrs. Wilson herself, and Susanna Locker of the *Evil in her Eyes*, so now at 17, she sells fruit in the Market, also Goody Drewets, daughter of Goody Lewis's husband, the *Dipper at the Well*, at Tunbridge Walks.

" You must note that Mrs. Norridge is removed from *The Pewterers* to the *White Hart*, a Linnen drapers, over against Hungerford-market in the Strand."

Sarah Gardiner, the wife of the late Famous William Kellitt, specialised in "curing Agues of all sorts, and wishes it to be known, that she still lives at *The Cock* in the Mint, in Southwark."

She says, that her late husband William, by God's blessing, and his diligent search into the Secret causes of that pernicious disease commonly called Ague, attain'd to the knowledge of an Incomparable medicine that speedily, safely, and infallibly cures all sorts and degrees of Agues, whether *Quotidian, Tertian* or *Quartan.*

" One *eminent* instance is that of an Apothecary of 72 years of age, who had lived forty years in Cheapside, and after ineffectually trying other medicines, by the advice of several Learned Physicians, was lately cured of a Quartan Ague and restored to health.

"Be it known, that Mrs. Sarah Gardiner late Widdow of William Kellitt, dwells in the same house where she assisted her husband in preparing and administering his medicine, and still continues by the blessing of God."

The virtues of the "True Spirit of Wormwood" are related by another "Widdow" named Mrs. Nevill, now a milliner, who lives next door to the *Ship*, near the great North Door of St. Paul's Church."

She tells us "that there is not any Herb that grows, that is a greater factor and friend to the Stomack than *Wormwood*.

"It removeth Stitches in the side and disperseth that melancholy water that hinders digestion. Take of this spirit in the morning 40, 50, or 60 drops in a draught of Rhenish wine, White wine, Bear or Ale, which you please; likewise I shall advise all persons that go to drink Epsom, Tunbridge, and Barnet Waters, to be provided with the Spirit of Wormwood."

Elizabeth Maris, who calls herself the "True German Gentlewoman" and was the mother of a High German Doctor, set up in practice for herself at the *Blew Ball* in Grays Inn Lane near Holbourn Barrs, next door to a Tallow Chandler, where her name is on a board over the door.

Elizabeth, with unusual modesty, excuses herself for issuing a bill, but like Dr. Saffold, she does not think it right, that "she should hide her talent in a napkin, which heaven has been good enough to bestow upon her for all your benefit and good."

She states that her "Parents and Husband were far skill'd in the Art and Knowledge of Physick, and from them she received the great secrets and experience through which she is able to cure any distemper of women-kind, including among other diseases Impostumes, inflammation of the lungs and Tertians of the guts."

There were apparently few disorders that Elizabeth could not cure, from ruptures to gravel. She claims to be able to " drive away all gouty pains in the Joynts, nay, though your arms and leggs were grown crooked and though you have kept your bed for many years, I do not doubt but to relieve you."

She concludes with a postscript, that " If any gentleman has any distemper not fit to be discoursed of to a woman, he may speak to my son, who hath practised Physick above Twenty years with good success."

CHAPTER X

MORE FOREIGN QUACKS

MUCH of the quaintness of the quack-doctor's bills, lies in the detailed directions usually given for finding their lodgings, which recall many of the lanes and courts of old London, now forgotten.

From these descriptions, one can almost follow the twists and turns of the narrow alleys, darkened by the overhanging gables, and picture the seeker of the quack looking out for the sign of the *Blew Ball*, or the "*lantern hanging over the balcony*," then groping up the tortuous stairs, and furtively tapping at the door of the doctor's lodging.

In such a house lived the famous Dr. Abraham Souburg of Gronigen, who heads his bill, "*Mille Opifex rerum medicaminis, Author and Anspex Primus lethaeos docuit depellere morbus*," and thus announces himself:

" Be it known unto all men, that to this famous City of London, this Renowned and well experienced Physitian, Cutter of the Stone and Oculist, has arrived." He declares, that " by God's assistance, he hath by his Art and Skill, gotten great Repute in the United Provinces of the Netherlands and in several Kingdoms and Dukedoms, having by his continual experience, acquired many fine and curious manual operations, not before

heard of, and hath many excellent Remedies for curing
Diseases incident to Mankind, which others have not
yet found out.

" He doth cure many Grievous Distempers in the

OPERATING FOR CATARACT
From a woodcut on a XVII Century bill

Eyes by manual operation, with *a needle of Gold, Silver
or Steel.* Even those who are blind by a Cataract, be
they men, women or children, he hath cured by God's

assistance, and brought them to their sight with speed, and without pain or smart, who could not distinguish by reason of their blindness, Fire from Water nor the Sky from the Earth, for there is no person in all the United Netherlands, nor in this famous City, who can operate with a Gold, Silver or Steel needle as he.

" He hath cured 184, both young and old, of blindness, by the help of the needle only, there being 313 distempers incident to the Eye.

" He doth cut and cure the Excrescences of Nature, be they never so Monstrous or Deformed. He is also a Famous cutter of the Stone, having attained to perfect knowledge therein, he being able sometimes to get the Stone out without an instrument and no person is made Lame thereby. Some persons use six or seven Instruments and spoil the patient, whilst he, at the worst, useth but one. He cut above 900 in the United Provinces, besides several in Flanders, Brabant, Germany, Munster, Euchden and other places.

" If anyone can produce me any person (by me cut) that hath any imperfection by reason of my cutting, I will give him Six hundred Rix dollars from the Province of Utrecht, for I cut 104 persons, whereof 96 were shortly well and brisk.

" This Doctor, Oculist, Cutter of the Stone, Cancer and Hair Lips, has a yearly sallery from the Lords of the State of Overyssel and from the State of Groningen. He is to be spoken with at his lodging in Hedge-lane, over against the Duke of Richmond's, near Charing Cross, having two round windows in the wall."

Another Renowned Dutch Operator who heads his

bill with the coat of arms of the City of Amsterdam, states he has cured "THOUSANDS AND THOUSANDS, as his Testimonials of several Princes in several parts of the world, can shew."

He begins his bill with an historical discourse, in which he says, "It is but a story and a fable, that the Morbus Gallicus began first in the Siege of Naples, for Monardes, that most learned Spanish Physitian will tell you, that it was very common before then in several parts of the World. If you understand Arabick or Chaldaick, Hebrew or Greek, read Algazel Alpharabius, Rabbi Joseph, Jetzira Onkelus the Pythagorean, and the very Cabalists of the first age of the world, they will tell you."

This learned Dutchman gives minute directions to his patients how to find his lodgings in the Strand which were "over against Exeter House (that is now pulling down), between the *Golden Cock* and the *Blew Anchor*, at a *Bookseller's House*, where you will see *Two handsome Blew Belconies, gilded*; but you are desired not to come to him the shop way, for there is a very fine conveniency to come the back way in the Savoy Alley; the first door on your left hand, near the Church, where you will see a *Blew Belcony, gilded*, and a *Green Lanthorn* with a candle in it at night, hanging over the Door to give you notice."

An Eminent Doctor of Physick newly come out of Poland next claims attention. A portrait of him heads the bill in which he states, that "so many persons have flockt to him, that he has been forced to give out these papers by the hands of his servants, to desire all persons whatsoever, to forbeare to come to him, unless it be for the cure of the morbus gallicus."

THE EMINENT DOCTOR OF PHYSICK OUT OF POLAND
From a woodcut on his bill

He declares that there is none in all Europe besides him, with the knowledge of such *brave* medicines as he has brought over with him, from the "old Chinese Doctor, to whom the persons of the GREATEST QUALITY resorted five and six hundred leagues, for such a cure. He is now dead at Breslaw in Silesia in June last, in the HUNDRED AND EIGHTEENTH YEARS OF HIS AGE."

He certainly had a curious method of diagnosis, for he says, "From seeing one or three of the Patient's Hairs, I will presently know what remedy is most fit for his cure."

He is to be seen at his house in Fleet street, betwixt the *Golden Lion,* and the *Three Golden Bucks,* next door but one to the *Castle-Tavern,* where there is a Hatch before the entry door, over against the sign of *The Lamb.*

" N.B.—*If any Lady hath an Extravagant Husband,
as so many honest wives have found to their sorrow, she
may have a remedy.*"

An Italian Doctor "who never was any STAGE
QUACK OR MOUNTEBANK," dwelt in Holburn,
within three doors of Brownlow-street, next door to an
Apothecarys and over against the sign of *The Magpy*."
He states that he has been very successful in the
" Speedy Cures of all sorts of Feavers which he certainly

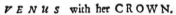

V E N U S with her C R O W N.

cures in *six days time*, the Dropsie in *three weeks time*,
and does also perfectly cure all convulsive Fits in *fifteen
or sixteen days*."

He declares that all these distempers are best to be
undertaken and will be more safely and more effectually
cured, " in the moneth of May and till the middle of
June."

" This Italian Master has brought with him out of
Italy, the " RIGHT ROMAN ORVIETAN," which he
sells at Half a crown the 3 ounces, or 6 ounces for Five

shillings, and so you may have as many ounces as you please."

"VENUS WITH HER CROWN" is the heading of another bill which begins with the lines:

" The sight hereof will make you for to think
But the Blessing of God we may after hint."

This quack implores "all sufferers to come unto him and he will help them, in as short a time as anyone, to the admiration of all people.

" Here is now come the Right Medicine Master, that hath cured so many hundreds and daily do ; therefor good people come unto me without fear, for time and opportunity is hereby lost.

"This High, Renowned Operator, Artist, Master or Traveller, hath brought over with him an excellent, rare, specifick, amiable and cordial Remedy prepared by a New Invention.

" He is approved of in many Nations by several Princes, where he hath cured many thousands. Therefor you have great cause to rejoyce that there is such a person for to cure you of these diseases. He has now purposely come to this Famous City, through the perswasion of many Eminent persons, who have had very much experience of him.

" I also cure any manner of Gout, let the humour be what it will, I presently give ease.   Therefor, come unto me for your own good and loose not this bill, that you may not be attacht with the vulgar here. Neglect not your own health, since God hath been pleased to send a means.

" Now for to let the world know his integrity, upright and honest dealing, he makes this Agreement, that he will not have any money for his Pains and Medicines, until half a year after that the Patient hath been perfectly cured. That is to say plainly,

NO CURE—NO MONEY

" This operator liveth without Temple-Bar, between St. Clement's Church and the Bar, next door to the *Crown Tavern*, at Mr. Gregson's house, a Meat-man, where you shall see these printed bills pasted at the door, and also a bill within Deverick's Court att the first door on the left hand."

A German quack named Frederick van Neurenburg, who arrived in London in 1698 took up his quarters at a house in St. Martin's-in-the-Fields, " next door to the Minister's house, opposite to the Church. Being a thoroughfare by the Church to the Strand ; a new house with a Hatter's-shop in the front and a free entry into Moor-Yard." This " Faithful Physitian," as he describes himself, states, " It is no wonder that clamarous Complaints and Confusion super-abound and Cruelty so aboundeth, and where so many vainly and arrogantly promise and undertake that which they understand not, without reason, nay, contrary to reason or possibility of Truth."

He then proceeds to dogmatise thus :

" The Art of Physick requires universal and experimental knowledge in Natural Philosophy which cannot be contracted and contained in the narrow circle of Domestick study and shallow Experience.

" Hence the difference is great between a Student and a Professor of Physick, and a Proficient and general experienced Physitian.

" The manner of curing and the goodness and proper uses of Remedies, the which Sloth and Ignorance hath divided into three faculties viz. Doctor, Chirurgeon, and Apothecary, the which of old, was, and yet is in some countries, intirely contained in one man, called a Physitian ; neither can any man be an accomplished Physitian who is ignorant in any of those three faculties."

He then proceeds to inform the public, that he has several " excellent soveraign approved Medicaments, Simples and Compounds, truly prepared viz, Stones, Minerals, Natural Balsams, etc, the which together with their hidden and excellent qualities I have with great charge, Labour and Travel gathered in several parts of Europa, Asia and America, where I have travelled and practised above thirty years." His preparations include the *Persian Balsam and Powder*, which cures all Fluxe and sharp corrosive Humours in the Blood.

The *Asian Balm*, the *American Balsam* and *Essence*, by the use of which the *Americans are generally strangers to the Gout.*

The *Japan Powder* which expels all manner of worms. The *Chinese Antidote* for rheumatism. The *Emperical Pill* for the Ague. The *Grecian* and *Turkish Antidote* which prevents fainting, The *Arabian Antidote* that prevents and cures the Ptisick and Consumption. The *Balsam of Gilead* for internal pains, and several cordial and pleasant *Physical Perfumes*, also several preparations that beautifie the skin without future danger, as frequently falls out by the use of mercurial waters.

All these medicines, he declares, are "bona-fide, positively and what I assert them to be, a parcel of which I afford for twelve-pence sufficient for several doses."

"Doubtless," he concludes, "there are more quacks and empericks in all arts than well qualified Professors altho' the General Frenzy of Humours, opinions and Al-a-mode customs conceil the subtiler sort of quacks, who by Quack Books and Opinions have proved as fatal to many, as Quack bills do to the vulgar and ignorant. Nay all are quacks in all arts and sciences, whatsoever, whether Theology, Law, or Physick who are not truly qualified, by art and nature for that which they profess.

"You shall not find *me* in the number of those who profess and promise more than they know or can do using the Refuse of Lyes, Equivocations, Evasions and Delays for their refuge. Considering the main circumstances which attend Publications of this nature, I shall only publish a few of these papers and bid a final adieu to the like for the future.

"N.B.—I may also be seen at my chamber *upon London Bridge*, near the *Gate*, at the sign of the *King of Diamonds*, being a Corner house."

The inventor of the HERCULEON ANTIDOTE, a Dutch Chyrurgion who lodged at the end of Threadneedle-street, near the Stocks-market in Three Nun Alley, at the Sign of *The Bursten Twins*, says, that "after twenty years study and travels in most countries of the universe, he hath attained to the knowledge of this medicine, which far excels any published in England, and for its excellent Specifick faculties is deservedly called the *Herculeon Antidote.*

" If any people are ashamed to come to me, they may have medicines sent them by any messenger, sending but a little note of their condition. I can cure Scal'd heads without pulling the Hair off, and draw rotten teeth and stumps with a touch."

John Schultius, a High German Operator who hailed from the *Three Flower Pots* in Holbourn-Row in Lincoln's Inn Fields states, he has " decided to continue in the city of London for some time ; for as a very expert oculist, he has taken away cataracts in the Eyes with his curious fine instrument with great success. He also healeth inveterate deafness in the ears, and though one could not hear the ringing of a bell yet he readily cureth them.

" He likewise draweth broken teeth and sets in artificial ones in their room, as firm as if they were natural, so that you may *eat to bite* with them."

An interesting bill illustrated with a woodcut, depicting the " Emperor of Turkey " witnessing an operation on his brother, and issued " with Liberty of the Colledge of Phisitians of the Royal Head City of London in England," announces the arrival of " a most Famous, German, Turkish and Imperial Physitian, who's like has not been in this kingdom."

The bill proceeds :—

" Be it then known to all high and lower persons, that this learned physitian who hath learned such a curious and strange art, which no other Doctor doth understand, and can cure all sorts of patients which are left off by others, has arrived. He can shew his testimonials from Three Emperors, Nine Kings, as also from Seven Dukes, and Electoral Princes, as the Romish, Turkish, and Japanese Emperors; he can shew his testimonial in 36 languages, which no other doctor can shew. He hath cured the brother of the Turkish Emperor, which was blind thirteen years and hath obtained his natural sight again.

"This German Physitian has travelled through three parts of the world. He lets understand, that he is so famous, that the like of him is not to be found; an Occulist, Stone, and Rupture-cutter, Medicinae, Chymicus, Practicus.

"He is a *Doctor beyond other Doctors* and gives counsel as to the effect of Witchcraft or unfruitfulness. This Physitian is also a *great artist* and draws teeth most artificially, whole teeth, little teeth, the roots of teeth, if they were so fast in the gums they cannot be seen, he knoweth to draw them with great dexterity and without trouble or pain. He puts in artificially teeth of Ivory, *Silver*, or *gold, as if they were natural.* He maketh black teeth white in a moment, which taketh a man's heart away to see it, and maketh loose teeth fast.

"He hath also brought with him, all sorts of smelling and well-tasting Teeth-Powder, to clean the teeth and make them white.

"If anyone hath occasion for these his Rarities, let them come to his lodging, and to persons of quality that send for him, he will wait on them.

" This said Imperial Physitian hath brought his Apothecaries shop along with him, and carries it where-ever he goes, for the good of his patients. He hath in his house in Moorfields, made by his art a Most Excellent Sweating and Bathing House, after the High German manner, in which he uses for his baths, the best smelling and odorous Herbs, through which, by the help of God, many diseases are cured thereby.

" Whoever hath occasion for this Imperial Physitian may come to his lodging or else send for him, and he will wait upon them according to their qualities. This Imperial Operator is at present in London and now liveth at a new house, the corner of White-cross Alley in Moorfields, next door to the Star Musick-House, where you may see the High German Spread-Eagle hang over the door."

This bill of the German quack is interesting from the allusions to early dentistry, which in England in the XVIIth century, was almost entirely in the hands of the Barber-surgeons, Quacks and Tooth-drawers. The instruments used, the chief of which were the Pelican and Davier, were of a very primitive des-cription and veritable instruments of torture. It is especially noteworthy that artificial teeth of ivory, silver and gold were then made, although gold dentures were known to the Etruscans and Romans in ancient times.

The introduction of baths of aromatic herbs in curative treatment, became common when the Bagnios and Hummums were established in London about this period.

CHAPTER XI

THE " SCURVY-QUACKS "

THE prevalence of scurvy in England in the seventeenth century is evidenced from the great
number of quack remedies that were exploited for this
disease. The use of the indigenous herb commonly
known as Scurvy-grass or Spoonwort which was chiefly
employed, goes back to the Middle Ages, when it was
cultivated by the monks in their physic gardens to make
an infusion which they administered to sufferers from
the complaint who came to them for aid.

Gerard in his 'Herbal,' 1580, remarks, "Our common
scurvie grasse groweth in divers places upon the brims
of the river Thames, as at Woolwich, Erith, Greenhithe
and Gravesend, as well as on the Essex shore. The juice
is given in Ale or beere. It perfectly cures the disease
called the Scurvie."

Scurvy-grass ale was specially brewed and dispensed
at St. Bartholomews Hospital in 1669. A brewer supplied the ale to make the Scurvy-grass drink and according to the Journals of the Hospital, in 1677, " the
steward was empowered to buy four measures of pewter to be used in the scurvy-grass cellar, but it was only
to be given by the direction of the doctor."

The quacks, ever ready to seize their opportunity

also began to make and advertise their own special preparations of the herb, which became very popular.

One of the best known, was Clark's Compound Spirits of Scurvy-Grass which was introduced in 1664. The bill states : " 'Tis some years since Mr. Clark first exposed his excellent medicine to sale, and (blessed be God) it has largely answered the end for which it was designed viz.: The health and welfare of his countrymen.

" The admirable vertues of these spirits and that universal welcome they meet with in the world, occassioned many counterfeits to be published, but their shams were quickly detected, and whereas they hoped to amend their credits by lessening mine, they did but present to the view of all honest men, their own ignorance and malicious folly.

" It is a Divine Maxim. That every Tree is known by its fruit."

Clark then proceeds to relate a number of cases in which his remedy " snatched people from Death's Door," in the year 1694.

Among them, was Mary Jones of Thetford, " who had not been out of her house for the space of Five years, but after taking two bottles, *Mary went to Church.*"

Clark's Spirit was said not only to cure scurvy but also Rheums, Toothache, Asthma, and Stone in the bladder ! But it did not cure Clark. " For it hath pleased the Almighty," the bill concludes, " to take to himself the said Mr. Clark, yet the said compound Spirits continue to be truly prepared by his Widow, at her Dwelling House in Naked-Boy Court, near Strand Bridge, by the Maypole in the Strand, which are sealed with her

Coat of Arms, the Three swords in Fess, Price 1s. a bottle."

The "Golden Spirit of Scurvy-grass" another preparation made by Thomas Blagrave, had a great vogue. On his death his son carried on the business of "the Noble medicine" of which he says, "his Father was the first author who prepared this "Golden Spirit" several years unmolested by counterfeits. It is now sold at Clerkenwell Green, the corner house of New Prison Walk, a *green door, a frame being over the door in gold letters with my coat of arms.*"

The sieur de Vernantes, who announced himself as a man of great learning, was the Inventor of an "Essential Spirit of Scurvey-Grass" for which he claimed wonderful virtues.

He says, " although of German birth, he graduated in Physick in those famous Universities of Montpelier and Padua in Italy, was sometime Professor thereof in Leyden in Holland, and chief chymist and Physitian to that great lover of Learning and Art, Arch-Duke Leopold; communicated by him to Hen. Clarke, Chymist and Apothecary of London and now by him prepared."

" This Noble Herb call'd Cochlearia or Spoonwort, from its shape and figure, changed its name and was call'd Scurvey-grass, from a peculiar and Specifick quality, which was found in it, to cure this disease.

" This noble Spirit, which from the hand of this great artist, I do offer to all who at this day suffer under the scurvey, and it also cures the Dropsey even to a wonder. It is to be had from Mr. John Ward at the *Pestle and*

Mortar in Panton street in Leicester Fields, Mr. Humphrey at the *Black boy*, a Cutler, next Whitehall, Mr. Markham at the *Seven Stars*, over against St. Dunstan's Church in Fleet Street, and *at his shop in Westminster Hall* and of Mr. Notts at the *Queens Arms* in the Pell Mell."

Robert Bateman another maker of " Spirit of Scurvy-grass," which he claimed to be the "*true and only* preparation," fought a wordy combat with his rival Blagrave and opened the battle with an amusing bill headed, " A gentle dose for the Fool turn'd Physician, or a brief reply to Blagrave's Ravings."

He begins, " I must beg the serious Reader's Pardon for condiscending to answer this clamorous Impertinence, it being in effect, but to Syllogize to an Oyster-wench or Wrestle with a Chimney-sweep, where nothing is to be expected in Return save Foul Language and Smut. Were my own interest and reputation only at stake, I should not regard the brayings of an Ass that so palpably discovers his ears, expressing so much malice, that if what he writ were as true as it is false, no wise man could credit him without forfeiting his discretion ; but since the Interest and Health (nay, lives) of people are concerned, to prevent his dangerous Imposing on the Vulgar who are apt to mistake Railing for Reason, Noise for Victory ; because correction being generally a necessary part in the cure of a Mad-man, who knows but this may do him Good ?

" The Case between us is thus : This Billingsgate Orator, not content to have counterfeited my Spirits of Scurvey-grass, impudently pretends himself the Author, and with the Policy of the proverb, ' To cry whore first——,' charges me, as if I had counterfeited them from him, abusing me in print with divers most False as well as Opprobrious reflections. Challenging him, since he had usurpt the Title of Physitian, to prove himself a graduate in either University or Licensed by the Honourable and Learned Colledge of Physitians.

" This unwelcome discovery put the man's choler (I cannot say his brains) into a violent fermentation and now, after seven weeks hard study and continual brooding on Envy and Malice, he has hacht this little Cockatrice, stufft with nothing but Slander, Lies, False-English, Nonsense and Impertinence.

" After this, he makes a clutter to prove the excellency of his Slip-slops, because forsooth : nobody is able to take half an ounce of them. As much might be said in praise of Aqua Fortis. Ignorant Scribler ! Sure this learned Travelling Mountebank, though apt to take pepper in the Nose, was never thoroughly acquainted with it, else he might know, that though it be hot on the palate, 'tis cold in the stomach !

" He is not able rightly to spell the very name of the Colledge he pretends to, not to mention the false grammar and solecisms frequent in his bills ; And as to his ten years travels in Terra Incognita we may safely conclude, 'twas only a Ramble through Berkshire and the Lands adjacent, with some Arch-Gipsy or at best a forc'd Pilgrimage to Barbadoes.

" But 'tis said the Gentleman is somewhat Craz'd, and very likely this Rhapsody was writ in a delirious Fit, therefore in charity, I would advise him to forbear

Tampering with Spirits, but rather to get the good old Remedy of Hellebore, and have a special care of his head this approaching Midsummer Moon and the ensuing Dog-Days."

Bateman then proceeds to extol the special virtues of his own remedy, the reputation of which he says cannot be sullied, and which may be got from his House in St. Paul's Chain near Doctor's Commons.

Having thus castigated his rival Blagrave, the irrepressible Bateman next makes an onslaught on his other competitor, the Sieur de Vernantes, whom he describes in his " Hue and Cry," as one who was " Lately shamm'd upon the World by one Clark, an Ale-Draper near Temple Barr." " Honest Countrymen! 'tis my unhappiness, not my humour, to be engaged in controversie. I take no delight in touching of pitch or answering the everlasting clamours of Billingsgate orators, but where a contest is unavoidable, it may sure be excusable.

" Several Triobulary Quacks have endeavoured to counterfeit my Spirits of Scurvy-grass, but still, like those foolish fires, which in dark nights lead people astray, these Meteors of kitchen-stuff-chymistry, soon become extinct, leaving a noysome flavour behind them. Of this class, this spring, there is started up one Clark (the first born of impudence) abusing the world with stuff he calls the ' Spirit of Scurvey-grass Compound ' of the preparation of the Sieur de Vernantes. Nothing can vex a Felon worse, than to be detected, so that modest and but just caution so enraged the animal, that it has since barked out a kind of apology, in which some

Abortive offers of wit are supplied with store of substantial lies and Railing.

"But in vain does the Blackamoor scrub himself; his fraud and folly is more conspicuous than before, for he is ashamed to tell us who this Worshipful Sieur de Vernantes is, or where he is to be found.

"May we not suppose him some Rosy-Crucian Philosopher in an Invisible cloak, whose person like his medicine's vertues, is become imperceptible?

"He dares not reply on behalf of his medicine, knowing well enough, that 'tis most pitiful counterfeit cheating trash, and the powerful specifick material he prattles about, is nothing in the world but an addition of Horse-Radish!

"This pretended de Vernantes is a WHIFFLING EMPERICK that has got as many names as a Popish priest. He was lately Doctor Jewel, when he huckster'd out Pills in Long-acre, formerly Doctor Bates, when he quacked it with Lozenges and having no success, he now sets out under this Outlandish-Mask to counterfeit my Spirits; but if he do not speedily desist, I'le *pull off his Vizard and expose his true Name*, which in truth will be the greatest disgrace that can be done to him. 'Tis true I have heard, he was once an Apothecaries boy in Oxford, but such a proficient, that to this day it would give an Artist a vomit but to see him prepare either Chymical or Galenical Medicine. As for his repute in Chancery-lane, an easie inquiry may satisfy. After shuffling from Chancery-lane to Queen-street, and thence to Castle-yard, he at last pitch'd his tent at Temple Bar, and to patch up a sorry livelihood adds to his two trades (chymist and apothecary) a third, viz. the laudable mystery of a *Drunkard Maker*, for though an apartment (as he magnificently calls it) of his Palace be let to a Coffee-Merchant, yet the rest of the Edifice in his own occupation is a Publick Mart, where you may daily be furnish't either with *Nappy Bub* or Compound Scurvey-Drinks at your pleasure.

" But I spend too much time on such trash. Come and taste gratis of mine, and be satisfied of the difference between the true, noble, rightly prepared Spirits and his sordid compounded Quackeries ! "

However, both the rivals died and Bateman's " Spirits " came to be made by one Robert Smith, while Clark's widow continued to compound his preparation for sixteen years after his death.

A certain Dr. Pordage of Leather-lane near Holbourn, was another maker of a " True Spirit of Scurvy-grass " which he sold at 6d. a bottle.

He states that, " by the new ingenious way of the PENNY POST, any person may send for it from any part of the City or Suburbs, writing plain directions where to send it to them. If for half a dozen glasses, they will be brought as safe as if fetcht by themselves and as cheap as one. But who sends this way, must put a penny in the letter (besides sixpence for each glass) to pay the carriage back, for nobody can think the profit great ; therefore a penny must be sent for every parcel. None need fear their money in sending by the PENNY POST, for things of considerable value are daily with safety sent by it, security being given by the messengers. There are houses appointed

in all parts of the Town to take the PENNY POST
LETTERS."

This bill is interesting as it shows that a penny local
post for letters and parcels was carried on in London
in the seventeenth century.

Among other quack remedies offered as a cure for
Scurvy, was Nendick's "Popular Pill." Nendick, in
recommending its virtues declares that this distemper
or popular disease is one peculiar to this country and
observes that 'some diseases familiar to some nations
we are altogether free from, as Leprosie (very familiar
among the Egyptians) Swelled throats, to the inhabitants of the Alpes, and the French-Pox in some parts
of the Indies.'

"The Scurvey, in short, is the undoubted cause so
many do linger and pine under so many tedious and
difficult Diseases, that I affirm with able doctors that
have lately seen the success of this Pill in divers
parts of England, as also at the 'Incurabile' in
Venice.

"They will be deliver'd to any messenger at my
House, at the *Two Black Posts* in Bell Yard in Carter-
lane, near St. Paul's Church."

The "Pilulae Anti-Scorbuticae," another remedy
"Against that Epidemick Disease the Scurvy," was
sold at the *Carv'd Posts* in Stonecutter-street, between
Shoe-lane and Fleet Ditch.

The maker recommends them, " for nothing but what
30 years experience of the galenical practice and above
20 years in the study of chymistry approves. Those
that drink the Spaw at Tunbridge, Epsom, Barnet

Astrop, Dulledge, Islington or any other medicinal waters, cannot do better."

The same quack sold a medicine called " Solamen Miseries," which he extols as an admirable remedy for Asthma and Rheums and as to the "Measles and Small-pox, *it brings them out to admiration.*"

The German quacks in London also sold a " Golden Elixir " called the " Herculeon Antidote," which they claimed to have special virtues for curing that " Popular Disease, the Scurvey."

The bill states, that in the Eastern parts of Europe our popular disease is the Scurvey which the " Golden Elixir " will cure, and then goes on to recommend the wonderful virtues of the " Italian Pills " which are specially good in Surfeits and after *High Drinking.*

As instances of their great value it is recorded, that "Mr. Davies on Thangue's Yard was cured of the Bloody flux who had three impostumes as *big as a hen's maw,* which was breeding 15 years, and was judged to be Ptisick.   Mr. Yangley's daughter, who had *worn away to an Anatomy.*   Mrs. French in Crown Court in Grub-street, was quite distracted, occasioned by a *Melan-cholick Passion* and was judged never to obtain her senses again, with this Elixir was cured.   Mrs. Price, a Strong-waterman's wife at Wapping New Stairs, who was *distracted* and *tore and broke all that she came near,* now perfectly cured.   Mrs. Cock in Irish-Court in White-chappel, a Latin schoolmaster's wife, who was swelled as *big as a barrel,* and *voided above* 60 *stones* and had made use of several physitians, is now perfectly cured.   Mrs. Warren in Soaper's Alley, in Whitecross-street, being

poysoned by eating Mussels and swelled from head to
foot, perfectly cured.   Then there was Mr. Feild, the
Sexton of the Dutch Church in Kattern-wheel Alley in
Whitechappel, was *worn to an Anatomy* and judged past
recovery, is now in perfect health.   Also Mrs. Fisher of
Plasto, at the sign of the *Green Man,* of the *wind Chollick* and Lameness, and Mr. Febs at the *Hand and Bowl*
in Barking, of a Ptisical Cough and Mixt Distempers,
all cured and now well."

CHAPTER XII

THE "UNBORN DOCTORS"—A QUACK ALCHEMIST

THE use of wine as a vehicle in medicinal preparations dates back to a period long before the Christian era. The early Greeks employed the wine of Cyprus to extract the properties of certain drugs, and this practise has continued throughout the ages to the present day, and survives in the form of the wines of Ipecacuanha and Iron still in the British Pharmacopœia.

The "Bloud of the grape," as it was called by Dr. Whitaker, in his book in 1654, was extolled by the quacks, and brandy often formed an ingredient in their nostrums. Whitaker believed wine to be a universal remedy against disease and its revivifying powers, no doubt inspired Ben Jonson to write his once popular ballad called:

" BACCHUS TURN'D DOCTOR

Let Souldiers fight for pay and Praise
And Money be the Miser's wish,
Poor Schollars study all their days,
And gluttons glory in their Dish,
   'Tis Wine, pure Wine, revives sad Souls,
   Therefore give us chearing Bowls.

Let Minions marshal in their Hair,
And in a Lover's lock delight,
And artificial colours wear,
We have the native red and white.

Your Pheasant, pout and culver Salmon,
And how to please your palates think,
Give us Salt-West-Phalia-Gamon
Not meat to eat, but meat to drink.

It makes the backward spirits brave,
That lively that before was dull;
Those grow good fellows that are grave,
And kindness flows from cups brimfull.

Some have the Tisick, some have Rheume,
Some have the Palsey, some the Gout,
Some swell with fat, and some consume,
But they are sound that drink all out.

Some men want youth, and some want Health,
Some want a Wife, and some a punk,
Some men want wit, and some want Wealth,
But he wants nothing that is drunk.
  'Tis Wine, pure Wine, revives sad Souls
  Therefore give us Chearing Bowls."

One of the most popular Cordials in which Spanish
wine played a prominent part, was Lucatelli's Balsam
which contained Venice Turpentine, Olive oil and
Spanish Wine washed in Rose water, Red Sandal-wood
or Dragon's blood, and Balsam of Peru. It was taken

internally in wine and used externally for burns and wounds. Originated by an Italian, it was much in demand in London in the XVIIth century and was sold by Charles Peter who lived in St. Martin's-lane, over against the sign of *The Castle*, where he also sold his " Famous Head Pill, a most rare medicine in most diseases incident to mankind, being most proper for all families to be provided with."

A " Drink " of another character was that exploited by Dr. Thomas Kirleus, who states that he is a Collegiate Physician and was Sworn Physician-in-ordinary to King Charles II.

One of his bills issued in 1691 reads as follows :

" In plow yard, the 3rd door in Grays Inn lane lives Dr. Thomas Kirleus, a Collegiate Physician and Sworn Physician in Ordinary to King Charles II until his death, who with Drink and Pill (hindering no business) undertakes to cure any Ulcer, Sores, Swellings of the Nose, Face or other parts etc expecting nothing until the Cure be finished. He has cured many hundreds in this City, many of them after fluxing which carries the Evil from the Lower Parts to the Head and so destroys many. The Drink is 3s. the Quart, the Pill 1s. a box with Directions ; a better Purger than which was never given.

" With another drink at 1s. 6d. a Quart, He cures all Fevers and hot Distempers without Bleeding except in few Bodies. He gives his opinion to all that writes or comes, for nothing."

An Alchemical philosopher, who professed to be ready to exhibit to the curious nothing less than the long-sought

Philosopher's Stone, took up his residence in "Lights Court near the *Kings Arms*, by St. Giles Church, where you may see over the door a printed paper." He announces that, " he hath brought along with him the work of a Famous Philosopher which is the True Matter and Stone of Philosophers and Naturalists, concerning Gold and Silver.

" It is a *Masterpiece*, and the most curious thing that ever was seen hitherto, where one may see without treachery the subject so much sought after by the Philosophers.

" This Gentleman will also shew some Sulphur and Mercury in their crudity, and also in their marriage, and although they be but in their first operation, yet the wonders of God, of Nature and of Art and a Philosophical Mine, in its vessel, are therein to be observed.

" It is meerly upon account of Charity, that this work will be exposed to the Publick view, to undeceive so many people, and to hinder so many Learned and Chymists, from wasting their estates and consuming their lives to no purpose, to come to the knowledge of the great work to which they shall never attain, as long as they shall make use, as the most part do, of matters which are quite contrary to that end.

" By seeing this work and by working, they may, if it please God, come to the knowledge of the True Philosophical Sulphur, Salt and Mercury, fixed by Nature, and see that possible which many believe Impossible, and they will afterwards employ their time upon a natural subject and common to all mankind which they shall never want, and will return the Gentleman thanks, for having shown them their errors and freed them from great expenses.

" Anyone may see this rare piece of work by giving only a shilling."

Rose's " Balsamick Elixir," which is described by its originator, as " The Most Noble Medicine that Art can produce," was a very popular remedy, " its incomparable virtues being such, that it gives or restores to Nature what's wanting and takes away what's hurtful.

" It is a signal Restorative for Consumptive persons and there is not such another preparation in the whole world.

" It cures the *English Frenchify'd* beyond all the other medicines upon the face of the Earth. It removes all pains in 3 or 4 doses and makes any man, tho' *rotten as a Pear*, to be *sound as a sucking lamb*.

" Whoever tries it, on my word, shall have just reason to thank me as well as pay me. And as I have set no value on anything here mentioned, you may be better satisfyed if you please to come or send to me at my Lodgings at Mr. Hamptons, a Joyner, in Hewit's-Court, near St. Martin's Church in the Strand."

The tradition attributing special occult powers of healing to a seventh son of a seventh son, goes back to an early period and has survived for centuries. In some remote parts of Wales to-day, such a person is believed to be endowed with extraordinary powers in the treatment of disease or in bone-setting.

This tradition was exploited by several quacks in the XVIIth century who laid claim to these hereditary powers, much to their advantage.

Thus we learn from a bill, " There is newly arrived in London an UNBORN DOCTOR, THE SEVENTH SON OF A SEVENTH SON, who (by God's blessing on his Studies) and more than 27 years travels, with most Famous and Eminent Physicians, has obtained to be an able Chymical Physician, Oculist and Chyrurgical Operator.

" He hath made a large demonstration of his great Abilities in Several Kingdoms, and as well in Hospitals and War-like Expeditions as in other places, for he hath obtained such a physical Method as never was in England before for the cure of all curable distempers in the bodies of men, women and children. He hath cured many in his travels of very sad and deplorable Diseases, which had been left off by learned Physicians and Chyrurgions as to be incurable, as he can show by testimonials from several Electorial Princes, Dukes and Persons of Quality."

After enumerating a number of Distempers which he had and does intend to cure, " by the Blessing and All-healing Divine Providence of Almighty God," he declares " his ability to be ready to treat Epilepsy, Rickets, Madness and Megrims.

" As a Chyrurgical Operator, this Unborn Doctor is able to take from the eyes, all Pin-webs and Cataracts in a quarter of an hour. He cures, to a wonder, those which are deaf even if for more than 20 years.

" He hath also a Great Secret for the cure of Crooked

children and Morbus Gallicus, a method never in England till now.

" All persons that have a mind to make use of him may come to his House, at the sign of the *Parrit and Rain-bow*,

AN OPERATION ON THE EYE
From a woodcut of the XVII Century

at the Lower end of Long-acre, near St. Martin's-lane end, when they may have his advice and medicines."

Another " Unborn Doctor " and " Seventh son,"

lived in Golden Lane at the *Golden Key* near Old-street. This gentleman, for the convenience of his West-end patients, was also to be spoken with on Mondays and Thursdays, next door to the Pump in Denmark Court, at the lower end of Exeter-street near the Strand.

This " Unborn Doctor " continues his bill in rhyme as follows :

" Resist Beginnings, late is Physick us'd
   When the Disease delay'd is deep infus'd.
   Now follow a catalogue of what he'll do,
   Be your Distemper old or new.
   First, Morbus Gallicus, you may be sure,
   He with speed will soundly cure,
   And as for the Gout, if any can,
   He'll ease or cure with any man ;
   But I confess unto you all,
   It is the Master of Physician-Hall,
   And as for the Stone,
   He never yet failed in none,
   If in the bladder it dissolveth not,
   He safely cuts it out,
   And cures the patient you need not doubt.
   Now as for Palsy, Fevers and all aching pains,
   He'll cure in Limbs, Nerves, Joints and Veins.
   For Wounds, Tumours, Cancers and Running
      Sores,
   In the Year he cures many scores.
   Now to all women he is a Friend,
   If they be sick or ill, he doth them mend,
   And as for children, of what e're they ail,

To cure them he'll never fail.
And as for those that deaf may be,
Or lost their sight and cannot see,
He by Art doth them restore,
Be they rich or be they poor ;
For every one of each degree,
That deaf and blind have been,
He hath brought to hear agen
Or see as well as e'en.
So 'tis for that very thing,
His Fame in England now do ring.
All ye that of cure do stand in need,
Make haste and go to him with speed ;
For be ye poor, sick, lame or blind,
He'll on his word, to you be kind.
So to conclude and make an end,
I to you this paper send
That you may see God's Gift is great to me,
By which I cause the Lame to go
And the Blind to see."

The *Pilulae in Omnes Morbus* or " Pills against all Diseases," which were popularly known as "Bromfield's Pills," had a great vogue in old London.

Bromfield who lodged at the *Blew Balls* in Plow-yard in Fetter Lane, relied largely on his testimonials to extol the virtues of his remedy. Judging from these he seems to have been a quack who travelled about the country, for he publishes the following letter dated from Chichester, the 19th of the 11th month, 1677.

" Doctor,

"These are to acquaint thee with a remarkable cure
that hath been lately performed with thy pills upon the
daughter of Edmund Stevens of the Parish of Apple-
drum near this city.

"She hath been extremely afflicted with tormenting
pains in her stomack and many times in all her limbs,
very much loathing her meat, not being in a capacity
to eat with her Father and her Mother at their table in
several years. Much hath been spent upon Physicians
and in Physick for her cure, but all in vain.

"She is now cured with taking thy pills, and hath
continued in good health since last spring. I might
inform thee of several others, but having no order for
it by those cured, shall say no more at present but rest
                    " Thy Friend,
                       " Rich. Carter
                                    Distiller."

Bromfield's Pills could be had from Mr. John Painter,
at his house called John's Coffee-house, above the Royal
Exchange in Corn-hil' ; Mr. John Bayns, Tin-man at the
Bird cage at Cock-lane end against Holborn Conduit ;
Mr. Flaxmore at the *Maiden Head* near Cherry-garden
stairs in Redrif-wall; and Mr. Edward Chandler,
Shoemaker, at Old Bedlam Gate going into Moor-
fields.

Another well known nostrum was the *Pilulae Lon-
donenses* popularly known as the " London Pills,"
which were said to be prepared by " a Physitian of many
years standing in the Colledge of Physitians in London,

according to true Rules of Art, good for prevention as well as the cure of all diseases."

Their inventor says, "by the advantage of a liberal education in the University, and many years experience in the practice of Physick in this city, the unprejudiced cannot but think me a person capable, not only of detecting the innumerable mischiefs arising from Quacks, but their ill-compounded and worse prepared Trash.

" Accordingly I have invented and for some time published, for the benefit of the publick these pills, which have justly brought their poysonous and absurd Physick under a deserved disreputation, all that are wise now dreading to trust their lives with those Pretenders.

" Not only the meaner sort of all ages and sex, but people of eminence, both for their rank in the world and their parts, have found admirable success in taking these pills.

" I take it Charity to caution you against some Cobbling Doctors, who having no knowledge of the Earth, pretend to do a great deal in the Stars. Do but read their bills and they will tell you of their skill in nonsense and their ignorance in Physick, notwithstanding their boasted Astrology. Believe them as little, who dare advise women with child to take as many of their pills as their body will bear, not regarding the Murther of Children.

" Most of these Mountebank Doctors also that commenced in a Shop, being vagrants from their trades, provide feigned letters of feigned cures as a pass for their Poysonous Mercurial Physick, from one town to another, having no other Patent commendatory to practise by, than the fob of a letter from some country fellow in recommendation of some Physick which he never took. These things being far remote from ingenuity or learning, I shall never trouble you with such."

David Perronet, who styles himself a Surgeon, appears to have specially cultivated the art of blood-letting and the cure of Toothache. He lived in Buckeridge-street between Dyot-street and St. Gile's Church, at the *Blue and White Ball,* the *Surgeons sign* being over his door.

Here he sold his " Universal Dentifrice which made black teeth as ivory, and a sure and speedy remedy for the worst Teeth-aches from such as be hollow and rotten; for be they never so raging or of long continued, this remedy will presently cure it by *Killing the Worm* in it.

" I further inform the Publick, that I *let blood* as cheap and safe as any of my profession. I make use of an excellent foreign method of bleeding viz., the observing of the proper times for it. 'Tis common in this country for People to use bleeding, either to prevent sickness, or be cured of some other slight illness, in which case they mind nothing else but their own leisure, or when they can best spare a shilling for it. By the proper time for it, I mean the Moon, which has undoubtedly no small Power over our bodies."

There was another practitioner of this kind called Edward Comport, who lived next door to the *Red Cow* in Shoe-lane, " who Letteth Blood and Draweth Teeth Dexterously for what you call for, also Cutteth issues for Sixpence."

The celebrated *Pulvis Benedictus* or *Worm Exterminator* required a book of fifteen chapters to record its wonderful power and the cures it effected.   The writer informs us, that a fuller account is given in a large sheet of paper, printed and done upon pasteboard, to

NEXT Door to the *Red-Cow* in *Shoe-Lane*, ſtill Liveth *E. Comport*, who Letteth Blood, and Draweth Teeth Dexterouſly, for what you Call for.   Alſo Cutteth Iſſues for Six Pence.

COMPORT'S BILL

be found in most of the eminent Coffee-houses in the Town.

The excellencies of this marvellous powder, which is declared to be " the only thing known, not only in England, but in the whole Europian World of the kind," are told in the pages of the treatise and in addition, the following stories are related. "The first is of one Mr. Stiles of the *Lock and Key* in West-Smithfield, who was practically *eaten by a worm 8 feet long*, and might still have been alive, if he had only taken the Exterminator, which is looked upon to be rather a *miracle* than a medicine."

Another extraordinary occurrence happened to Mr. Stubbs, a surgeon living at Stratton Ground in West-minster, who was " about to embalm a Gentlewoman who had been dead eight and forty hours. "When working his operation, *her heart leapt out upon the table*, and out of it he took a worm *as thick as an arrow*, with *two heads*, one like a *serpent*."

How these stories helped to sell the Exterminator, it is a little difficult to conceive, but probably, like the worms in a bottle, the quacks were so fond of displaying, they were designed to frighten the spectators into using the remedy whether they required it or not.

The originator, who lived at the *Golden Ball* in Devonshire-street without Bishop's-gate, thus concludes: "Since it hath pleased Almighty God to send such medicines as will prevent these fatal evils, I think it a great error in those that neglect them."

" A cure for Melancholy which is offered to distracted friends " by Mr. James Newton, who lived on Clerkenwell Green, throws some light on the treatment of the insane in the XVIIth century.

He states in his bill, that " he seeks not applause, yet would he not be vilified. 'Tis not more my own than others good I aim at ; nor do I seek more to cure the Rich for reward, than the poor gratis ; but I labour by all means to cure both, rather than keep any in my House for advantage. I might give many instances of it, but I'le name only three of the Parish where I live.

" The first was a woman put to me by the Church-wardens in 1672, who was very much given to *swear* and *tear*, having very grievous sores made by binding her in bed with cords, yet was she perfectly cured in three weeks.

" The second was a man void of sense and reason, who when his hands were at liberty, most vigorously beat himself and tore the hair off his head. *He was perfectly cured in four days.*

" The third was a man put to me by the Overseers of the Poor in 1674, whose distemper varied from the other ; wherefore, because I would not say he should be King Charles II, he commanded the standers-by to take off my head, for he would be King Charles whether I would or not. *He was perfectly cured in six days.* The truth of what I here affirm will easily be confirmed, if those that doubt hereof, will but apply themselves to me at my House. Now, if any skil'd in these distempers object anything, I am very willing for their satisfaction, if I may have liberty, to take three persons out of Bedlam that have been there several years, and to bestow all necessaries upon them gratis."

A notorious quack and mountebank already mentioned, who lived at the *Sugar Loaf* in Ram Alley, right across Fetter-lane, was Ben Willmore. In a bill he issued in 1680, he claims to heal ulcers, impostumes, cure pains and inflammations, and continues his commendation in rhyme.

" Are you Sick, Lame, Blind, Deaf, Dumb, come
       away,
   To this skilful Doctor and do not stay.
   Try Willmore, a cure you will thereby,
   For Honest dealing is his Policy ;
   And when you have done, pray prove so kind,
   Respond your Candid censure as you find."

He expresses himself ready to " Cup you after the
German manner, Purge you after the English manner,
or Sweat you after the Turkish manner. You may be
neatly blooded, your teeth or stumps dexterously drawn,
have Issues curiously made, and Setons put in your
neck, safely, for " sixpence a piece and welcome."

" THE OLD MADE YOUNG," is the heading of a
bill addressed to those who desire to make their lives
happy and long.

"I will not pretend," said the writer, "that I have
known my great Restorer cure any distemper, excepting
one, and such a one, as I believe never was helped by
any medicine but this, that is to say in LOVE AFFAIRS
both in OLD MEN AND WOMEN.

" This I suppose many will laugh at, and few will
believe, but it has that *miraculous operation* that it
renders *old men and women of three or four score,* as
youthful as those of *twenty or thirty years of age.*

" Thus it is an extraordinary *Prolonger of Life* and
may be had at my house in Nevill's Alley in Fetter-lane."

Another curious character was George Fairclough, a
quack oculist, who at one time had been blind himself.

According to his bill, " he hath given such eminent

proofs of curing all sorts of eyes of late in London, and hath so oft cautioned all persons against quacks, mounte-banks and old women, hath now done each a won-derful cure at the Bath, upon a person, by one breaking into his house by night, first striking the man down with a piece of iron, then battered and flatted his face and twisting his hands in his hair, placed his thumbs in the corner of both his eyes and by violence forced them out.

" In this barbarous manner he was brought to me, as dead as a sheep's eye cut out of its hed ; yet with God's assistance I replaced his eyes and restored him to perfect sight again. This being notoriously known to the whole city and all gentlemen and ladies here.

" The Mayor and Justices sent the criminal to prison for the same."

CHAPTER XIII

THE BEAUTY-SPECIALISTS

AT the time of the Restoration and after the period of Puritan severity had passed, women again began to seek those aids to beauty, which had been introduced into this country in the early part of the century.

Perfumes, powders, face-washes and various cosmetics brought over from Italy and France were exploited by the many beauty-quacks who began to flourish in London.

Some of their bills read very like the advertisements prominent in the columns of our ladies papers and magazines to-day.

The neighbourhood of Mayfair, even in those days, was the happy hunting ground for the beauty specialists, and one of them who established herself in Bond Street, issued the following bill.

" Amongst so many famous persons that have apply'd themselves to study the so necessary art, is a Lady well-known and reputed among the Gentry, who has studied for the space of above forty years, and has performed many wonderful cures in France and elsewhere."

She was evidently something of a chemist as well as a

physician, for she says, she had studied all manner of
" Physick, Chymical, Gallonique, Hermetique, as well
as Chyrurgical and Fermatie.   She also extracts Potes-
tates, and Impetu's, and the three Principles of all
manner of mettals, minerals, animals, vegetals and of
mirrh.

" She makes all kinds of Liquors, Salts, Powders,
Pills and Opiates ; whereby she extracts out of the body,
all manner of venoms, poysons, plagues, purple spots,
measles, great and smallpox with few Doses, and in so
very short a time as can't be imagin'd nor believ'd
without one sees it ; as also all manner of chollicks of
what cause soever, Malignant vapours and others, in a
moment's time as she has experimented many times.

" Besides these and other distempers, this Lady
preserves Youth and Beauty.   She *beautifies without
any paint* and increases the Radical Humour in some
and restores it in others, corroborating the spirits,
animals or vitals and the whole body, so as to live (God
permitting to old age) without any sickness, but on the
contrary always lusty, strong and healthy.

" In a word, without any Disparagement of many Able
and Eminent Professors (for every one hath his particular Gift of God) she durst without any boast or bray,
challenge any one to do more and to go beyond her in
the Practice of this Art; and if anyone surpasses her, she
is willing to give over and no more to profess this Art.

" Let none slight her, before they have seen and heard
her and tryed her medicines, all that she aims at being
chiefly the Glory of God and the good of mankind in
general.

" She desires also to be better acquainted among
Persons of Quality and Gentry, that other Ladies, when
they see and Know her Capacity and Great Skill, may
for the Honour of their sex be emulated to follow her
example.

" She will use every body so kindly that none shall
have cause to complain.

" Let every one then, consider that such a Person as
this Lady is, is a *Pearl and a Treasure,* for she works
almost Night and Day for the good of mankind, which
a great many Persons of the first rank can testify. Fur-
thermore, this Lady cures the most inveterate Distempers that's possible for man or woman to have, which
modesty will not permit to name. *She cures without
seeing them.*

" Her Eye Water, so necessary for old people, must
also be mentioned, as by the use of it, a Person of above
sixty years of age may recover as good a sight as a young
person.

" Therefore, come to her and you will know more of
her ability. She lives at Mr. Trout's in Bond-street, near
Picadily, the second House on the left-hand side."

The beauty-quack's subtle and persuasive methods,
are instanced in an address issued by a " Gentlewoman,
who lived at *the Surgeon's sign,* just at the corner of
Coventry-court in the Haymarket, near Pickadilly."
Her bill begins as follows :—

" God the author of all things, to make man in love
with his wife in her state of innocency, he made her

smooth, soft, delicate and fair to intice him ; I therefore, that woman might be pleasing to their husbands,
and that they might not be offended at their deformities
and turn to others, do commend unto you the Virtue
of an eminent and highly approved ' Balsamick Essence,'
with several other Incomparable Cosmeticks, faithfully
prepared *without Mercury.*

"This ' Balsamick Essence ' takes away the broadest
freckles be they never so long standing, wrinkles, morphew, tan, sunburn or yellowness, in Thirty days, and
renders the skin plump, soft, fair, bright, smooth and of
a lovely colour.

" 'Tis of that mighty Influence, that the like was never
found out to Beautify the Face and there is nothing of
paint relating to it.

" The aged it makes appear fair and young, and preserves beauty to their lives end. 'Tis a most delicate
thing to anoint the Face with when the smallpox begins
to dry, for it certainly prevents all scars and pits.

" Price one shilling each bottle of the Noble Balsamick
Essence.

" A Super-super-excellent paste for the *shaking and
trembling* of the *Hands* after *hard drinking* or *otherwise*,"
was another novelty prepared by this ' Gentlewoman.'

" It will also make them smooth, soft and of a delicate
white colour, that although you were to *Scower Brass
and Pewter* and to make *Coal fires* every day, yet nobody
will imagine you to do *any such drudgery*, as hundreds
can testify."

The use of mercurial preparations and their attendant evils, had been recognised in the XVIth century, when mercury was frequently employed in cosmetics and applications for the skin.

Another " Gentlewoman " who " liveth in Great Suffolk-street near the Haymarket, at a *Jeweler's house* with a *Red Balcony* " announces, that she has attained the " Most Rare Secrets in the World for Beautifying the Face, as many thousands can testifie. Those who have had their Faces utterly ruined by Poysonous washes, so that the skin has been reduced into a perfect wainscot colour, by her Art she can restore."

As well as her beauty preparations, this Gentlewoman states that she has "physick to perfectly cure the Gout and finds no ingredient wanting but *Faith*, which if the patient *will bring with him*, she doubts not but by God's Blessing, to perform the rest."

The use of the word " wainscot " to describe the complexion, was common in the XVIIth century, when the skin assumed a yellowish or parchment-like colour.

A " Gentlewoman " who claimed wonderful virtues for her preparations dwelt in Surrey-street in the Strand "at the *Corner house* with a *White Balcony* and *Blue Flower pots.*"

" Her Most excellent Wash to Beautifie the Face also cures all Redness, Flushings and Pimples. Takes off any yellowness, morphew, sun-burn spots on the skin and takes away the wrincles and driness caused so often by mercurial poysonous washes ; rendering the *worst of faces* fair and tender and preserves 'em so. You may have it from half a crown to Five pound a bottle.

" You may also have Night masks, Forehead pieces,

incomparable white pots, and *Red pomatum for the Lips,* which keeps them all the year, plump and smooth and of a delicate colour. She has an admirable Paste to smooth and whiten the hands, with a very good Tooth-powder which cleanses and whitens the teeth. You may have a Plaister and Water which takes off Hair from any part of the body so that it will never come again. She has also a most excellent Secret to prevent the Hair from falling, causing it to grow *where it is wanting* on any part of the head. She *shapes the eyebrows* making them perfectly beautiful, without any pain, and *raises low foreheads* as high as you please ; And colours grey or red hair to a lovely brown which never decays, changes, or smoots the linnen. She has excellent Cos-meticks to anoint the face after the Small-Pox, which wears out any scars, marks or redness, and has great skill in all manner of Sore eyes."

No modern beauty-culturist could do more.

The prejudice against red hair was apparently com-mon at the time, and the repeated recommendation of applications to anoint the face to prevent the pitting of the skin following small-pox, recalls how prevalent this disease was in London in the XVIIth century before vaccination was known.

Dr. Corlett makes the interesting statement, that in the time of Charles II, the Court Beauties and women of fashion looked in envy upon the immunity enjoyed by some of the dairy-maids of Gloucestershire, from the disfigurement following an attack of the dread disease.

The Duchess of Cleveland, in 1670, when once joked with the possible loss of the King's favour through the disfigurement caused by small-pox, is said to have replied, that she had nothing to fear, as she had suffered from cow-pox; a remark which significantly foreshadows Jenner's great discovery in the following century.

It was through the endeavours of Lady Mary Wortley Montague wife of the British Ambassador to the Ottoman Court, in 1717, that the physicians of London were first persuaded to try the method of inoculation then practised with some success in Turkey, as a preventive of small-pox.

Talc, which is now so largely used in the preparation of face-powders, especially in America, is no new discovery. It was employed in making cosmetics in England in the XVIIth century as evidenced in several bills.

A " Gentlewoman " who lived at the *Green Ball* in Chiswell-street, over against the Artillery-wall, near *The Archer*, claims to have been the first to sell " The Water of Talk " in London.

She announces, that there is now made at the *Green Ball*, being the first place where this preparation was made in England, that " Most Famous and well-approved Water of Talk and Pearl, the clearest and brightest of all waters, and is of that excellent virtue for the clearing of the Face, that in a short time, will turn the Brownest complexion to a Lovely White.

" It is now used by most persons of quality in England, it being of that excellent vertue, the longer it is kept, the better it is. She hath also Rare Washes and Powders, and also Forehead pieces both leather and linnen, and an

excellent Water to make hair grow. An excellent Oynt-
ment that will take hair off from the forehead in a
quarter of an hour, an incomparable *Red Lip Salve* that
heals all sores and chops in the lips, a marvellous
" Powder of Talk," the best of all powders for clearing
the skin ; also Vizard-masks to be worn at night, and
gloves to make the hands smooth and white."

The forehead pieces referred to, were strips of soft
leather or linen impregnated with a mixture of sper-
maceti, wax and oil, which were placed on the forehead
at night when going to bed to keep the skin soft and
prevent wrinkles. Vizard-masks for the same purpose
were made of similar materials, and were used to cover
the upper part of the face, slits being made for the eyes.

A Beauty quack who lived in Wine-office Court in
Fleet street, at the sign of *The Acorn*, included fortune-
telling among her other accomplishments, and states,
that "she will resolve to her own sex all manner of lawful
questions. She also hath most excellent Washes for
the Face, and has been experienced by persons of the
greatest quality, for they make the face most lovely,
plump, smooth and beautiful. She hath most excellent
Pomatums of several pleasant scents and for several
profitable uses. She hath also a most rare and easie
Art in shaping the eyebrows and in making low fore-
heads high ; she can cause the hair to grow thick and
colour it to what they please, and to continue so. She
also sells the usual washes, pastes, toothpowders and
balls."

One of the favourite cosmetics of the Court ladies of
Charles the Second's time, was the " Princesses Pow-

der," which was so-called, " because four Princesses, whose great beauty was renowned throughout Europe, used it with such success that they have preserved their skins and their beauty, with an air of youth, till Seventy years of age."

The bill recommending this famous preparation states, that " Madame de Montespan, with whom the King of France has been so much in love, very well knew, by this little artifice, how to please that Prince and she has made her beauty famous over all the habitable earth. Madame de Montespan has no fine nor delicate skin naturally, but by means of this Powder, which she has used all her life, she had preserved the fineness and delicateness of it, so that she does not appear above eighteen or twenty years of age though she be above fifty-five.

" But as Mr. René, chymist and apothecary at Paris is dead, and that he was the only one that knew the Secret of composing it, he left by writing, to Peter René his son, the Secret to make the same.

" It is commonly known by experience, that this powder produces extraordinary effects, and the said Mr. René has been requested by several persons to send it into foreign countrys and particularly hither into England, where the climate is extremely harsh.

" It has already had extraordinary effects on persons that have had *very ill looks*, and they have now recovered Lustre and their Beauty by means of this powder.

" In a word, it has the vertue to take away all Redness, all Pimples and Frecles, and generally all ill things that occur in the Face, and maketh the skin so fine, smooth and dilicate as Sattin ; as you may experience

by putting it upon your hand a little of that enclosed
in the Pacquet.

" There will be put to all the Pacquets that shall be
sold, the seal of him that made them ; to the end, to
prevent the cheats that may happen by persons pretending to have found the Secret of its making.

" Anyone that has a mind to have this powder may
have it at Mrs. Joanna Nehellon near the *Blackmoor's
Head* in German-street, over against the church, also at
Mrs. Elizabeth Jackson's over against *The Ship*, near
the Maypole in the Strand, and the price of the Pacquets are from sixpence to five shillings."

A " Gentlewoman " who dwelt in " Red Lyon Court,
but now removed to Racket Court near Fleet Bridge,
the third door on the right side, hath obtained with
much difficulty, a *Secret that no one else hath*, from a
great Lady in Paris, now dead, who sold it there to the
Queen and Court, for above Twenty thousand pistoles
in one year.

" You may have it from her for half a crown to five
pounds the bottle.

" She can alter Red or Gray hair to a most delicate
light or dark brown, which will continue so for ever
without any soil or smooting."

A Hair-dresser who " cuts and curls all Ladies and
Gentlewomen's Hair extremely fine, after the French
fashion," lived at the *Cross Keys* on Ludgate-hill, next
the *Rainbow Coffee-house*, and had an " Extraordinary
Essence that preserves the hair in a wonderful manner, and it is of that singular vertue, that it will actually

prevent hair shedding after the small-pox, and is to be used instead of Orange Bath or Pomatums."

"There are a great many Beautiful Ladies who have but indifferent hands, and would be overjoyed to make them white, if they knew how," writes a "Gentlewoman," with some truth, in proceeding to recommend the virtues of her "Only Delicate Beautifying Cream."

For the

FACE, NECK, and HANDS.

"She also hath a curious fine white for the Face and Neck, entirely without mercury or any such hurtful thing in it ; it being a new thing never before published, 1s. a pot. She also sells a 'Cholick Tincture' and 'Daffy's Elixir' and the 'Famous Purging Sugar Plums, without any mercury at 12d. a dozen.

"The 'Only Delicate Beautyfing Cream' is daily sold in great quantities to the Court and the greatest of the quality, who continually express their abundant satisfaction in the use of it.

"This Gentlewoman liveth up *one pair of stairs* at the *Sugar Loaf*, a Confectioner's shop, over against Old Round Court, near the New Exchange in the Strand."

Dr. Paul Chamberlaine's Wonderful Necklace could also be obtained from her. In the bill concerning it, the doctor expressly desires that the World may know, that he absolutely advises the wearing of this Necklace by all children for their Teeth.

"In and about London," he states "12,000 children yearly, die of their teeth, whereas out of great numbers of children who have only worn this Necklace, we do not know of one that has died. A Treatise writ upon it and dedicated to the Royal Society, shews how it naturally performs all these surprising effects, from a secret harmony and sympathy in Nature between this Necklace and the Human Body."

At Nixon's Coffee-house, the inventor of the " World's Beautifyer " could be spoken to if desired. " This never failing medicine prepared without the least Mercurial or Poysonous Ingredients, in a week's time, perfectly cures the worst of *Red Faces* in Man or Woman."

It should be noted that, " if any person of distinction wishes to be waited on at their houses, in sending notice where they shall be attended, and if any in the country send the colour of their hair, age and what condition their face is in, to their friend in Town, they may have it delivered to them with direction, they giving security for the sum agreed upon, the lowest price being two guineas."

> " As medicines from unskilful Quack
> Their Force and Efficacy lack,
> So from a skilful hand ('tis known)
> The Patients cur'd and not undone."

The " Water of Talk and Pearl " evidently had a great vogue. There were several rival makers of this cosmetic in the field, and among them was Pecune, a famous Italian quack. His preparations were sold by a " Gentle-woman " who informs us that, " there is another Person who hath lately set forth bills entitled ' The Fountain of Beauties,' who does pretend to something of this nature ; But nothing to the purpose, he being only taken in by me for sometime as my servant, till he thought he had gained experience enough, then ran away in my debt and is now gone further distant to deceive others.

" If any persons Faces are wrincled or damaged by using poysonous powders, which are too frequent in this age, there is none like that made by the ' Famous Italian Pecune,' whose ' Water of Talk and Pearl ' will bring them to their former complexion. It will create beauty where Nature has been defective, as it hath been experienced by many Persons of Quality who have been sending many Leagues for it.

" He hath also a Water, that will bring *Hair on a BALD HEAD*, if the party be not too old, and an excellent Water to make the Hair curl.

" Likewise, you may have Talk finely prepared, both Roman and English, and any other wash made, as Myrrh Water, May-Dew sublimated, or Blossom-Water called the French-Wash.

" Also ready drawn Spirit of Mint and Saffron, Spirit of Orange, pleasant and very good against the Scurvey, Rosa Solis made the Italian way, most excellent in consumption and a High Cordial.

" For all these you may be pleased to repair to the

Vera & Viva EFFIGIES
Stephani Draper, *M. D.*
And Man-midwife,
Ætatis Suæ x' γ'. "Εἰκοῦι Τροῖς, A. D. MDCLXXXVI.

Blew Ball in Blew Ball Court, over against the *Ship Tavern* in Salisbury Court in Fleet Street, or at the *Green Ball* in Chiswel-street, turning up Bun-hill, over against the corner of the Artillery-wall and next door to the *Anchor*."

The last in our gallery of Beauty-quacks is Dr. Stephen Draper, who in 1686, issued a bill that he strictly directs is to be " *Presented to none* but *Ladies, Gentlewomen* and *Civil Maids.*" Draper, who was not without

a sense of humour, was skilled in the art of flattery and
dedicates his address to :

" *Beloved Women,* who are the *Admirablest Creatures*
that ever God created under the *Canopy of Heaven,* to
whom therefore, I have devoted my studies to the preserving of your Beauty, Health, Vigour, Strength and
Long Life."

The following are some extracts from his bill.

" Ladies, beauty is a Blessing of God, and every one
ought to preserve it, in fine, they do as much offend
that neglect it, as they do that Paint their Faces.
Therefore I commend unto you the Virtue of My ' Water
of Pearl,' with several other cosmeticks for the face
faithfully prepared without Mercury.

" My ' Water of Pearl ' defieth corruption and
adorneth the countenance with a lovely Rosie complexion, and renders the skin soft, fair, bright, smooth
and of a lovely colour. The aged it makes appear young
and Illustrates Beauty to a wonder. Nay, it addeth to
Nature's Masterpiece, a sensible and visible advantage
and is but ten shillings a bottle. I also make a
Rare Powder, that makes Black and Yellow teeth as
white as Ivory and kills scurvey in the gums.

" A Water that brings hair on a Bald head and an
unguent that heals the Chops in the Lips, and gives
them a cherry colour, beautiful to beholders.

" 'Tis undeniable," he adds, " that Nature has so
Illustrated some Women with beauty, that they think
they cannot be beholden to Art ; *yet Nature without
Art is frail,* as we see in plants and flowers which perish

for want of Artificial means or fade by unskilful hands,
so it is with Beauty.

" Ladies, Draper with his Pearl Water doth out-doe
All other Washes, and the pride of Nature too.
Altho' Dame Nature she hath made some women
    Fair,
Use his Cosmeticks you'd be indued past compare ;
Yea, your adorned Beauties will transporting prove,
That who so gazes must be ravish'd with Love.
Your Beauty will be a surpassing Throne of Graces,
Like a Bright Illustrious Queen you'd charm all faces
What Kings humbly offer Scepters, Diadems and all,
Nay, Kingdoms compar'd with Beauty are but small.
Abuse your time no longer, but be advised,
To let men know your Beauty to be prized,
Let vertuous Modesty your Beauty grace,
For it will make each charm more lovely in your face;
And also will the Roses with your Lillies joyn,
 Besides the Sweet Carnation with the Jessamine.
Further yet, you'd find it doth a Factor prove,
To barter such men's hearts that trade in chastest
    love,
Nothing more firmly wins, there's nothing sooner
    can,
Than a female modest beauty, alure fond heart of
    man.
And he that lies panting on a vertuous breast,
Let him with all love and beauty be doubly blest,
In Beauty and in Vertue, the Graces all appear,
Women's beauty adorned shines ever in its sphere."

Another quack from Italy thus announces his arrival in London : " A Doctor (who being lately returned from his Travels) who hath by his long and daily study and practise abroad, particularly in Italy, Spain, and Portugal, discover'd and found out a safe, sure, and speedy and easy way or method to cure all persons, is at the Sign of the *Queen's Arms* in Stock's Market by Beard-binder Lane.

" He hath brought over with him from Italy and which is sold by his wife at the place above, a most delicate wash for the Face, besides Cold Cream and other rare things (which cannot be inserted here) for the use of Ladies and others, never made use of in this kingdom."

CHAPTER XIV

THE PLAGUE QUACKS AND OTHERS

THE time of the Plague was the quacks great opportunity, and they flooded the Town with advertisements of their so-called infallible medicines and remedies for the dread disease. The posts of houses and corners of the streets, were plastered with the bills and papers of " Ignorant fellows, quacking and tampering in physic and inviting people to come to them for remedies." Among the quack medicines were " The Sovereign Cordial against the corruption of the Air," the " Infallible preventive Pills against the Plague," "The only True Plague Water" and a score of others.

" A list of preservatives and medicines against the plague that were mostly used " was published in 1666, from the " Sign of the *Angell*, neere the Great Conduit in Cheape-side."

" As preservatives against this disease," says the writer, " Eate every morning as much as the kernell of a nut of this Electuarie, which I shall keep always ready for you, or of Treacle mixed with Conserves of Roses or Diascordium, the quantitie of two white peas.

" Let your chambers be ayred morning and evening with good fires, wherein put, Juniper, Frankincense, Storax, Bay leaves, Vinegar, Rose water, Rosin, Turpentine, Pitch, Tarre or some of them.

"When you go abroad, chew in your mouth the root of Angelica, Gentian, Zedoarie, Enula campane or the like.

" Likewise twice a weeke, take a scrupell of the ' Pestilenciall Pill,' in two pills, when you goe to bed or an houre before supper.

" Also I have prepared Tablets to weare about the necke, of which I did see great aid and experience the last great sicknesse, as also Pomanders to smell to.

" As remedies after a person is infected, after bleeding, Mithridatum, one dramme and a halfe ; of the best London Treacle one dramme, and mix with them Carduus Benedictus or Angelica or Scabious Waters."

Even the Inn-keepers entered into competition with the quacks in selling plague drinks as the following announcement from the *Intelligencer* for Aug. 28th 1665 shows : " An Excellent Electuary against the plague, to be drunk at the *Green Dragon* Cheape-side at Sixpence a pint."

Shortly before the epidemic reached its height, a French quack-doctor arrived in London who announced that he had discovered a method of preventing the disease, which had proved successful in Paris, Lyons and Toulouse. His invention, which he called " Angier's Fume " was soon in great demand. He succeeded in deceiving Lord Arlington the Secretary of State and the Privy Council, who ordered the Lord Mayor and Aldermen of London to " Give Angier all encouragement and distribute his medicaments."

His famous fumigation was afterwards found to consist of Sulphur, Saltpetre and Amber.

An elaborate bill was issued in 1670 by John Russell, who styles himself a Professor of Physick and Oculist, at the "*Two Blew Posts* against Gray's Inn in Holbourn."

Surrounding a portrait of the " professor " are illustrations of various operations he claimed to be able to perform.

The first, on the left, depicts a case of rupture. Second, Extracting the stem of a tobacco pipe from a man's mouth where it had been lodged for three days. Third, Couching a cataract. Fourth, Extracting a nasal polypus. Fifth, Trepanning a man whose skull has been fractured. Sixth, An operation on the Eye. Seventh, Operation for fistula. Ninth, An operation on the breast. Tenth, Operation for Hare-lip. Eleventh, Cutting off a great wen. Twelfth, Tapping a patient for dropsy. Thirteenth, An operation for rupture.

Russell declares that, " these pictures present what I have cured by manual operation, that without boasting, I may truly say, few as yet performed the like.

" There is above 100 diseases of the eyes and few understands their cure, which causeth so many blind, that a good oculist might have prevented, for it is not enough to say he is a linguist, if he have not studied to be an Oculist. That will not serve the patient who cries, ' Give me ease and sight or else I am for ever blind.'

" I have many Sovereign medicines that are friendly to the Vital Spirits, which I have prepared out of animals, vegetables, and mineral mettals, that I am not confined to the use of a few in practice, for there is many thousands, that if they have not medicines at a cheap rate must perish.

" The reason for publishing this, is for the sake of those that cannot go to the charge of fees and are not able to pay for such costly courses of physick, as is commonly used."

John Newman, a quack who had a stage on Moorfields in 1679, also claimed to be a most expert Chyrurgian. " I shall not trouble your ears," he says, " to give you an account of the operations I have performed in many parts of England and other places beyond the Seas but shall only mention what operations I have perform'd on my Stage since March 28, 1679, when I cut a large Wen the *bigness of a penny loaf* from off the throat of Robert Bond, a carman, and is now very well. On April 2, I cut a large Rupture from Michael Butts living next door to the Signe of the *Crown and Lamp* in Gravel-lane near Petticoat lane. I cure the Poor of Wens and Hair lips, for God's sake." Newman was also to be found at his Lodgings at Mr. Richard Shores, at the Sign of the *Prince of Orange's Head* on Windmill-hill, in Moorfields.

At the " Signe of the *Red Ball* in Bartholomew Close, with *Two Black Posts at the Door*, near unto Smithfield-gate, lived an " Expert Operator " and maker of the *Never Failing Pills*.

" There never was more Pretenders to cure than there is now," he states, " but Friends, have a care how you fall into the hands of such *ignorant Pretenders*, for if they once but get you into their clutches, they will use you as unmerciful as they are unskilful. Therefore, be not ashamed to come in time. COME TO ME !

" My ' Never failing Pills ' are so prepared, that the

tenderest patient may take them. They are excellent good for Seamen to take to sea with them, for they keep their full vertue for Seven years.

" A private lodging may be had if required, and the house is so private, that no notice can be taken of your coming to him, from six in the morning till ten at night."

E.M. a " Doctor of Physick " and the maker of the " Universal Scorbutick Pills," was an advocate of advertising and begins his bill with a brief historical discourse. " The Honour and Esteem of Physick," he states, " was in former ages so great, that Kings and Princes did own and allow medicines of which they were authors and inventors, to be called by their own names. Physicians of the greatest fame delighted in the preparation and tryals of medicines, so were they ambitious their names should give title to the medicines. But this last Age, revolting from the ingenious labours of the Ancient Heroes regarding the Art of medicine, let it fall into the hands of Tradesmen. Medicines thereby fell much lower in repute.

" Physicians now reviving the primitive practice, are at present discouraged from offering the products of their art to the world, for fear of scandal and being accounted in the number of these Quacks.

" But the publishing of medicines by the learned, which will prove most advantageous to the people, should be encouraged among skilful and experienced artists, that they may not lock up their rare inventions and fortunate experiments, confining them within the narrow limits of a private practice. If a printed sermon or any piece of learning cried about the streets be no disparagement to the work nor the author, why the publishing of a medicine : Again, if Persons of Honour and Quality expose their cattle and produce of their land at Market and Fair, why not men of Arts the products of their learned ingenious labours ? "

The Honourable Robert Boyle was a pioneer in scientific chemistry and one of the Founders of the Royal Society, but according to a quack who hails from " the *Gridiron*, with out the Bars in Whit-chappel," he was also the inventor of an *Effectual Pill*.

In his bill he states, " That the world may no longer be deceived by the false and ignorant pretenders to Physick, of which this City has more than enough ; I present to all the ingenious, the most *Effectual Pills* of which the ever-honoured Esquire Boyle was the Author.

" And 'tis to be lamented, that so many thousands suffer yearly by these distempers, not knowing where to address themselves to honest, able men, so the publisher humbley conceives 'twere a pity, wondrous pity, to conceal or bury so precious a Remedy.

" True, it is indeed, that the world (for the sake of a few notoriously ignorant Physick Pedlars) are ready to dis-esteem all bills exposed to view, but if men will still continue in that humour, they may as well hate the Scripture, because the Devil sometimes takes an Argument from it. They may likewise condemn all trade by sea, because some few suffer shipwreck. For which reason, the publisher did for a long time decline all thoughts of printing, but on being last prevailed upon by the unanswerable perswasions of worthy men, he is to tell the world, that if they will avoid the horrid torture of ill cures, if they will disappoint the irrecoverable disgrace of the fall of the Nose, in a word, if they will prevent the slaughter of the Body and the Rape of the Purse, they may address themselves to a Physician, learned in all causes as well as this."

Another famous remedy was the " Grand Balsamick and Health-Procuring and Preserving Pill," which the proprietor, John Hooker of St. Paul's-Chain near Doctors Commons, declares to be the *most pleasant in the World.*

" It is a compound," he says, " of the most costly and precious ingredients that ever Art or Nature yielded, and is adapted to all ages and constitutions. Among other truly remarkable properties, it draws away the corroding humours from the lungs, and by that means *Surceases the Toothache.* It fortifies the Optick Nerves and by that means preserves and strengthens the Sight. Nor is it less beneficial to purge away the Dregs of unconcocted wine, which occasions morning nauseousness of the Stomack, the decay of appetite, and that Sottish Dulness that attends hard drinking.

"These pills are sold by Mr. Grainger, at the *Three Neats Tongues* in Chancery-lane ; Mr. Collier on *London Bridge,* under the Gate ; Mr. Rickards, Haberdasher of Hats, at the *Hat and Gun,* Bishopsgate, and Mr. Thornton, at the sign of *England, Scotland and Ireland,* in the Minories.

The " Pilula Salutiferens " or the Health-Bringing Pill, is said by the proprietor, to have been first prepared by the " Famous Dr. Sydenham for his own use, who afterwards prescribed it with incredible success throughout the vast extent of his Laborious Practice."

"It is a composition of all the richest Cephalicks and Salubrious Stomaticks in Physick, and is especially good for the head, to purge the brain, quicken the senses, and leave a liveliness upon the Spirits."

Piercy, Lownds and Buckworth, were three rival Lozenge-makers, who flourished towards the end of the XVIIth century. The former, who lived on the *Postern*, next door to the *Black-horse* near Moorgate, "whose ability and skill, are so well-known for his Famous and Most approved Lozenges for these 27 years," comes forward

THE INVENTOR OF ' PILULA SALUTIFERENS '
From a woodcut on the bill

with a bill in which he states, that "some persons of late, have taken a prejudice against him, and have taken on them to make lozenges and undervaluing those of Mr. Piercy which are so highly approved by the Queen Dowager's most Excellent Majesty, as by other great and eminent persons of this nation."

To this, Theophilus Buckworth of Mile-end Green issued a counter-blast to vindicate himself, "From the wicked designs of his rivals, and to expose their villainies."

He says, " I intended to rest thereupon in silence, but yet they, still pursuing their wonted practise in Scandalous Libelling, I am once more inforced, though I shall not trouble you with a recital of their many impudent untruths and scandals published by Piercy and Lownds against me, the Author and operator of the said Lozenges.

" When Piercy began to make Lozenges, Lownds issued bills against him, but when they met and Piercy would sell him lozenges, such as they are, for five shillings a pound, then Lownds, for his own profit utterly disclaims Buckworth's, and combines with Piercy to scandalize my Lozenges.

" Lownds pretends great care of the people's health, but being told that Piercy's Lozenges were not so good as Buckworth's, his answer was, he cared not, for his Sign was the Sign of the *White Lyon* still, and if they were ' Brickbats ' sealed up, he could sell them.

" Lownds, then finding his design to fail herein, hath gotten one Buckworth to make him lozenges, and now the said Lownds being undeceived herein, sells them again, pardon his mistakes.

" They have the Impudence to publish, that Buckworth was convicted by a Legal tryal, and that he was indicted at Sessions and durst not appear to justifie himself, but this is notoriously False.

" It is true, they contrived, an arrest against me and prosecuted by Richard Adrian, a Minister (such a one as 'tis) who is brother-in-law to John Piercy, who for his mischievous acting therein, was, the last General Sessions, Indicted, and by the Court committed to the

New-Prison, and at the next Sessions will receive punishment according to his deserts."

Thus apparently ended the bitter dispute of the three rival makers of lozenges, now long forgotten.

The " Metallick Eagle," was the name of a wonderful chymical powder, that was sold by R. F. Philalethes who lived at the *Sun* in Gutter-lane near Cheapside.

In his address he states, " whereas about four months last past, there was published a little paper in these words, viz :

" The Rich may command, be bowed unto and flattered for rewards, but the Poor may intreat and be rebuked with a scornful look.

" Therefore, these are to give notice to all that are poor in City or Country, that are either sick or lame, may under God, have cure of the worst diseases, curable for nothing, if they repair to the *Sun* in Gutter-lane.

" Yet, Nothing without God. Since which, there hath been many wonderful cures performed by a Chymical Powder called the ' Metallick Eagle,' the which medicine, and cures hath given great cause of admiration and brought great resort to the place.

" I believe, there is not the like medicine extant, unless the Grand Medicine of the Philosophers, and I know not any that dares to pretend to have obtained it yet. Thus, I thought good to warn the innocent and detect the presumptious, in the world, as now it is time, may no longer be deceived or imposed upon.

     Farewell, your friend

       R. F. PHILALETHES."

The marvellous properties of Fletcher's Powder, which is described as a " Noble and Excellent Panacea " are set forth in a bill also issued by the originator in 1679 from his House at the *Sun* in Gutter-lane near Cheapside.

Fletcher states that his " powder is so wonderful a Friend unto Decaying Nature, that whatever unnatural, destructive and health-opposing matter it shall meet with in the body of man, it will radically exterpate, and drive out, and in its place constitutes a Healthy Body, as hath been proved by thousands in the City of London.

" It powerfully cures that disease, *A la mode d' Engleterre*, with all its symptoms, and there is nothing able to withstand its power, against all other diseases but against death."

Fletcher then waxes eloquent as to the nature of his great remedy.

" It is," he says, " a medicine of a Solar (or Gold like) nature made by Art most subtile, penetrable and capable by its splendent beam, to dispel those mists in the air, which cloud and darken the Sun of the little world of man ; and he that hath such medicine as this, need not so much mind the uncertain indications, diagnosticks and the like verbal impertinences, which serve only for ostentation."

Fletcher recommends his powder for Madness, Inflammation of the Brain and all violent pains in the head, and the dose was a spoonful taken in Wine, Ale, Beer, Sider or Mead. He makes an interesting allusion to the use of medicine chests on ships at sea, and says, " this medicine is of great value and may save life at

sea when the *doctor's chest* may fail." He further gives
a list of people in various parts of the city who sell it.
These include Captain Newman at his Coffee-house in
Talbot Court, in Grace-church-street; Mr. Blunt at
the *Black Raven*, over against Bedford House, and Mr.
Jer. Howes, Scrivener, *near the Spittle* in Bishops-gate-
street.

A Physician who issues a bill from the *Heart and Star*
at the Dyers' Arms, next to John's Coffee-house in the
Great Old-Bailey, relates some cures that have resulted
from taking his *Special* " Elixir Proprietatis," or Chymical Balsamick Spirit. Thus, Mrs. Parker, a Ribbon-
weaver in Nicholas street on Shore-ditch, " who was in
a languishing condition for two years and given over by
many Physicians, some affirming that she had *a Devil
in her*, by the Blessing of God, was perfectly restored to
health in *three months*. John Wooton of Puddle-Dock
of the dropsey in *three weeks*, and the son of Mr. Hunt,
a Tobacco-pipe maker, over against the *Sugar-loaf*, in
Salisbury Court, of rickets, wherewith he became a
cripple, was cured in *two months*."

" Lady Moor's Drops," recalls the period when
many ladies kept a manuscript book, containing
recipes for domestic ailments with which they doc-
tored their dependants or lent them to their friends.
Mr. Wells who lived against the *Blew Bell* in Long-acre
near Drury lane, claimed that he was " the only one
that hath the true receipt from the Lady's son."

" The Super-excellent vertue of these Most Famous
drops," he states, " universally known throughout this
kingdom, by persons of all ranks who have us'd the same;

the great effects wrought by them has obliged me (for publick good) to make them as noted as I can to the world. They never fail in curing consumptions, dropsies and all manner of coughs.

" When people look yellow, black, green, or of several other sickly colours, by taking these Drops they'l look for the future of a young, brisk and lively complexion.

" Beware of a Gentlewoman who pretends to have the true receipt of these inestimable Drops.   It is prov'd she *never had* the *true* receipt.

" The price of one shilling and sixpence a bottle is charged ; being known to prevent counterfeits by my coat-of-arms.   That is Vert a Cheveron Ermin between three martlets argent.

" They are sold at the ' Golden-candle stick ' in Cheapside, at Mrs. Unwins, Perfumer, under the Piazza in the Royal Exchange, against the Star Coffee-house ; and Mr. Harbarts, a Perfumer, next door to the *Horse-shoe* in German street, St. James."

" Glad tidings to unfortunate patients and to all persons languishing under any stubborn distemper," is the greeting of a " Proficient in Physick, Surgery and Chymistry, at the *Golden Ball and Surgeons Arms,* in White-Lyon street, near the Seven-Dials in St. Gile's-in-the-Fields.

" The like has never been offer'd to the world before, for by his diligent study and practice in Their Majesties Service, both by Sea and Land, he hath obtained to many great secrets in Nature, relating to the cure of all Distempers incident to Human Bodies.

" His ' Elixir Mineral,' erradicates and carries off

most stubborn distempers, and is the most Infallible remedy yet known for the King's Evil, Tetters and Ringworms. He likewise hath the greatest secret yet known for the gout, by which he will engage to bring a person to walk about in 3 or 4 days, or a week's time at the furthest, and desires no reward till it is performed."

"The Olbion," popularly known as Badger's Cordial appears to have been a pioneer effort in preventive medicine, as it is extolled not so much as a " Cure-all " as a *prevention* "against all Contagious, Pestlential and Epidemick diseases."

John Badger, the inventor, who calls himself a "Doctor in Physick," lived in St. Swithin's-lane, over against the sign of the *Carpenter*, next door to the *Crown*. He claims his " Cordial to be a Specifick for the cure of Agues and Intermitting Fevers of all sorts viz., Quotidian, Tertian, and Quartan, if prudently and seasonably made use of.

" It encreaseth appetite, cures cold and pains in the head, coughs and Rheums. For all these, there is not a more Noble Medicine to be found, and is more safe and by far exceeds the ancient compositions of Mithradate and Venice Treacle, those grand medicines of the Apothecaries, which no one of them ever did or could make true.

" It deserves to be treasured up by all families in the room of those adulterate and vicious compositions, which the Company of Apothecaries are now going to prepare at their Common Hall, to the scandal of their fraternity and the future ruin of this Society."

Reference is here made to the Laboratory for the preparation of medicines, the Society of Apothecaries decided to set up at their Hall in Water Lane in 1690, with the object of securing the purity of drugs employed in the making of medicinal compounds.

It is very probable that Badger's cordial was a preparation of Peruvian bark, which, about this time, was being used in the treatment of ague and intermittent fevers.

A quack who lived next to the *Two Black Posts* in Old-street Square, announces that he sells a " Great Cordial Antidote " against all Pestilential Diseases and Venoms, called Elixir Vitae.   He also has an Essence of Honey endowed with many vertues, which cures Fainting or Sounding Fits and the Falling sickness. His " Laudanum of Cordial Pill against Surfeits, Small-pox, and Melancholey, causeth pleasant sleep, giving rest and ease in those in trouble or in pain."

" Panchimagogum Febrifugum " was the name given to another fever cure, which also probably contained Peruvian bark.   Its inventor directs that, " you must take it all at once, that is one sealed paper, in the pap of a roasted apple, as big as a hazel nut ; before you rise in a morning fasting, and within one hour after, drink some posset-drink or some broth made of fresh meat or fresh butter, and then keep your bed for three hours, if you wish to be cured of all kinds of Tertian Agues or other Intermittent feavers.   All the operation of it is done in 3 hours.   This remedy will keep good during the whole life of man."

CHAPTER XV

CINCHONA, or as it was originally called Peruvian or Jesuit's Bark, was first introduced into England about 1658, and like several other drugs which afterwards came to be recognised as of great value, was originally exploited as a secret remedy as a cure for ague.

At first it naturally commanded a very high price and the apothecaries made large profits from its sale. During the latter part of the XVIIth century, the Physicians were involved in a long and acrid dispute concerning the charges made by the apothecaries for their drugs, and this is reflected in a bill, apparently issued by Dr. Charles Goodal, who was a regular practitioner.

It states: "Whereas it hath of late been the Endeavour of several members of the Physicians Colledge to reform the abuses of the Apothecaries, as well as in the prizes as in the composition of their medecines; this is to give notice for the Publick Good, that a superfine sort of *Jesuit's Bark*, ready powdered and paper'd into doses, with or without directions for using it, is to be had at Dr. Charles Goodal's at the *Coach and Horses* in Physicians Colledge in Warwick Lane, at

4s. per ounce, or for a quantity together £3 per pound ; for the reasonableness of which prizes (considering the loss and trouble in powdering) we appeal to all the Druggists and Apothecaries in Town, and particularly to Mr. Thair, Druggist in Newgate-street, to whom we paid full 9s. per pound (? ounce) for the use of ourselves and our friends. And for the Excellency and Efficacy of this particular Bark, inquire of Dr. Morton in Grey-Fryers.

" I am to be spoken with at prayers at S. Sepulchre's every day, but the Lord's Day, at Seven in the morning and at home from eight in the morning till ten at night.

" The Poor may have advice (that is nothing for nothing)."

Dr. Goodal certainly employed an ingenious method of advertising himself, but it is obvious that the 9s. per pound, is an error and should have been 9s. *an ounce.*

To this bill, Mr. Thair or some wag, ever ready to take advantage of a quarrel between the physicians and the apothecaries, thus replied : " Whereas there has a scandalous paper been lately dispers'd abroad, reflecting upon the honour and conscience of a member of the Colldge of Physicians, as if the Prizes he exacts for his medicines were more exhorbitant than any he complains of in the Apothecaries.

" This is to inform the world ; that 'tis resolved by the Secret Committee of the said Coll. nem. con. that it is as unsuitable to the Dignity of one of his character to be contented with the humble profit of Ten pence in the shilling, as 'tis insolent and unreasonable in their

vassels, the apothecaries, to demand it. But because
he designs for the future (out of his condescending
temper of mind) to obviate all clamors of that nature,
he has determined to take down the ' Coach and Horses '
and to dispose of them to the first chapman, so that
being at no other extraordinary expense, but mending
shoes and stockings, he may be enabled to afford the
better pennyworths, and therefore henceforward, all
that have occasion for any of his Superfine Bark, may
be furnished at Physician's Hall with what quantity
they please at 3s. per ounce, or allowing for his great
trouble and pains in powdering it, 1*d. per drachm!*

"WHICH IS TOO CHEAP IN ANY MAN'S OWN
SENSE. As the Colledge Tributary, Dr. Saffold, has well
expressed it in his immortal poem : It infallibly cures
the Stone, Dropsie and Gout, taken inwardly and out-
wardly, Rubb'd on the gums it hastens the cutting of
the Teeth. It cures Convulsions, Botts, Kib'd heels,
Farcy, Childblains, Corns, the Mange, Spasms, also
Religious and Love Melancholey, Meazle in swine,
Christians and Prating in Elderly Persons, and makes an
admirable Beauty Water.

> " But what should here repeated be by me
> The vast and barbarous Lexicon
> Of Man's Infirmity."

Cotgrave in his " Treasury of Wit and Language,
(1655) " has left us a picture of the quack of his time
in his description of " Dr. Pulsefeel " :

" My name is Pulsefeel, a poor doctor of Physick
That does wear three-pile velvet in his hat,
He paid a quarter's rent of his house beforehand,
And (simple as he stands here) was made doctor
beyond the sea.
I vow, as I am right worshipful, the taking of my
degree cost me twelve French crowns and Thirty
five pounds of butter in Upper Germany.
I can make your beauty, and preserve it,
Rectifie your body, and maintaine it,
Clarifie your blood, surfle your cheeks, perfume
your skin, tincture your hair, enliven your eye,
Heighten your appetite ; and as for jellies,
Dentifrizes, dyets, minerals, fricaseas,
Pomatums, fumes, Italian masks to sleep in,
Either to moisten or dry the superfices,
Faugh !
Galen was a goose and Paracelsus a Patch,
To Doctor Pulsefeel."

Among the quacks who set up their stages on Moorfields, was Thomas Rands, who after he had gathered
a sufficient number of spectators would thus deliver
himself :

" My business in this famous City is to let my Fellow
Christians know the excellent qualities of my medicines, which I sell to the Rich but give to the Poor.

" Imprimis. Is there any old woman amongst you
troubled with the Pimple-Pamplins, whose skin is too
short for their bodies. See, here is my ' Anti-pamphas-

tick Powder' or my 'Sovereign Carminick,' which discharges Ventiferous Humours of what kind soever and will reduce you to soundness of body in the Twinkling of a Hobby-Horse.

"Then, see here is my 'Balsamum Stobule Swordum' or an Ointment that's good against all cuts, green or canker'd wounds.

"Now suppose any honest man amongst you has hurt or cut himself with either sword, gun, or musket, spit, Jack or Gridiron, glass bottle or pint pot; by the help and application of this my celebrated Balsam, they are immediately cur'd without giving themselves the trouble of sending for an illiterate surgeon, who will sooner cleanse their pockets of money than the wound of its infection.

"Then Gentlemen, see here is my 'Purando's Tankapon Tolos,' that is to say in the Arabian language, the 'Wonderworking Pills,' the excellent quality of which is hardly even known to myself. They purgeth the brain from all Crassick, Cloudifying Humours, which obstruct the senses of all superanuated maids. They make the Curratick Directick and the Directick Indirectick in their lives and conversations. Then take three of these pills in a morning *Jejuno stomacho*, with two quarts of *Aqua Gruellis*. I am none of those fellows that set an extravagant value upon themselves, merely because they ride upon spotted horses, but my medicines have made themselves and me famous throughout Asia, Africa, Europe and America.

"It was I, cur'd Prester John's Juggler's wife of a fistula in her elbow of which she died. It was I, prevented the old woman at Exeter from running headlong into a Wine-cellar. It was me, and only me, that cur'd the French Dancing Man at Amsterdam of the Consumption in his pocket. It was me, who perform'd an excellent cure upon Captain Nonsuch, Commander of the Nonnomen Galley, who had a Cannon ball lodg'd in his little finger, likewise the carpenter of the same ship who had swallowed a handspike."

(The Zany's Song)

" Here then of great sense
     At a little expense,
     May furnish themselves with a packet,
     Or if any one's poor
     That has been with a W——
     For sixpence he need not lack it.

     Though money be scant,
     Yet physick you'll want,
     If ever you come into danger,
     Then Beaus come and buy it,
     Prove, judge and try it,
     Or privily come to my chamber."

Gilbert Anderson was a notorious quack well-known in the neighbourhood of St. Gile's between 1665 and 1680, who lived near the Inn significantly called the *Cradle and Coffin*, in Cross-street. He was a canting rascal who turned religion to account whenever he could get the chance. He had evidently travelled abroad and gained some experience as a surgeon's mate on a ship.

" All praise and glory to be given to God alone," is the heading of his bill, in which he states: "he hath travell'd through the most part of the known world, and so acquired the most rare secrets of Physick and Chyrurgery during 35 years, 12 of which he spent in the quality of Chyrurgeon to a ship, in the wars of Candia, in which time he never made a voyage without fighting ; and yet was so happy in his undertaking, that he never dismembered any man, neither did any dye under his cure of their wounds ; but on the contrary, he cured many that were to have been dismember'd by others.

" He can speak indifferently the languages of the Turks, Moors, Italians, Spaniards, Portugues, French, Dutch, Swedes and Danes, and for the truth of his great skill, has the three following certificates. The first states that 'the Rector, Church-wardens and others, ancient inhabitants of the Parish of St Gile's-in-the-Fields do certify that Mr. Gilbert Anderson, hath by God's blessing performed many eminent cures upon the sick, lame and diseased, to his great commendations, and we never heard that any of the patients which he undertook to cure, either missed of cure or died, by reason of any miscarriage of his cure.

"'For which miraculous operation and his singular charity to the Poor, we humbly conceive him to be very deserving of employment.'"

This is signed by Nathaniel Stratton and Henry Hobgood, Church-wardens. 18th of April 1673.

He also prints a similar certificate from the Churchwardens of the Liberty of East Smithfield of St. Botolph, without Aldgate, signed by Duell Pead, Minister, and

Thomas Fryer and Henry Fletcher, Church-wardens. Dated 30th of March 1679.

His third testimonial purports to be from the Burgomaster and Councillors of the City of Congal in Sweden, who testify, that " the Respectful person, Doctor and Physician, Gilbert Anderson, lived in Congal for two years, and has cured many persons both there and in Gottenburg and Melstrand. This certificate is for his safety in his travels to Denmark. Sealed by the Town Seal on the 18th September 1665."

He says, " he hath no remedies that cure all Diseases, but he hath for each several disease a proper remedy, and undertakes to cure Rheums that fall from the head to the teeth, the black and blue marks caused by blows, in 48 hours, and hath a plaister for the sciatica or hucklebone gout which will banish the pain in a wonderful short time.

" He solemnly promises in the Presence of Almighty God and the Holy Host of Heaven, not to undertake any but such as he hath good hopes are curable by him.

" He hath lived ever since 1665 in the Parishs of St. Martin's and St. Gile's, where the ablest Doctors of all Nations converse, who have thought it no disgrace both here and abroad, to ask his advice in difficult matters and have found it good to admiration."

He adjures his patients, to " be not scrupulous in observing times, lest you provoke God to wrath, for with Him, all seasons are proper for restoring his people to Health."

Anderson thus advertises for an apprentice. " If any good honest man have a well-educated son, that he would have instructed in Physick, this doctor is willing, upon any reasonable terms, to undertake it, and make him equal with the best Outlandish Physicians. He can be spoken with at his dwelling at the lower end of Cross-street in Hatton Garden, near the *Cradle and Coffin*, next door but one to a Carpenter's yard, and right over against a Meal shop."

"The Famed and True Lozenges of Blois," a popular remedy for coughs and colds, were sold at most of the Coffee-houses in the city at the end of the XVIIth century.

A bill recommending them states : "The Salt and Sulphurous Vapours particularly in London, joined with a foggy and moist air which begets Rheums and Coughs, lead many learned physicians to seek divers Remedies, amongst which the particular preparation of the Juice of Licorish is rightly called the True Balsam of the Lungs.

"I do not pretend," says the maker, " to have been the first to make this excellent remedy, but I have highly improved it with the full approbation of their Majesties and most of the Nobility attending the Court.

"The White juice thus prepared, hath been shown unto and been both recommended by word of mouth and approved in practice by many eminent physicians, and sold at most of the great Coffee-houses about the City. They bear my Coat of Arms on the box, being the Three Boars Heads and a Bloody Sword."

"Drops of Comfort," was the soothing name given to a quack remedy that was recommended to give " im-mediate relief and to effect a perfect cure, in the tor-

menting pains of the Chollick, and makes those that
take it Fresh, Fair and Lively for many years."

" Drops of Comfort " were distributed at 5s. a bottle
by Mr. John Paradise, perfumer, next door to the
Cross-Kea Tavern ; Mr. Robert Chilcott, perfumer, in
Westminster Hall, and Mrs. Ann Farmer at the *Unicorn*
in Fleet-street.

Richard Mathew, the originator of the " Famous
Pills," lived at a house by the *Lyons Den* at the *Tower*
and next gate to the *By-ward.*

In 1662 he published a book entitled, " The Unlearned
Alchymist, his antidote, or a full and ample explanation
of the use, virtue and benefit of my Pill ; with directions to make and prepare the drink now in use called
coffee."

He dedicated it, " to all that are sick under pains,
aches, gripings, and divers diseases, but more especially
such as are poor and have no money, Rich, Mathew, your
brother and companion in the Kingdom and patience
of Jesus Christ."

In a long preliminary epistle, he describes the wonderful virtues of his pill and states that " a man of
middle strength should take about the bigness of a
grey pease and drink a little sack after it."

He claimed the pill to be a great antidote to poisons,
and relates the case of " a gentleman who drank 200
grains of Opium at one draught, then swallowed a pill
and yet is in very good health."

His account of " the drink called coffee, now so much
used " is interesting at this period. " The Coffee
berries," he says, " are to be bought at any Druggist,

about three shillings a pound. Roast them in an old frying-pan, then beat them to powder and pour through a lawn sive. To a quart of boiled water put in one ounce of your coffee and boil gently for a quarter of an hour, and it is fit for your use."

Mathews died the year after the publication of his book, for in 1663, we find that his wife issued an additional treatise called: "A pretious Pearl, in the midst of a Dung-hil, being a true and faithful Receit of Mr. Richard Mathew's Pill, according to his own practice, recorded in writing under his own hand in 1659, and Presented to the world by Mris Anne Mathews, amongst many sad complaints of wrongs done her and the commonalty and her deceased Husband."

Her chief complaint is the wrong done to her as a widow by imitators, who declare " Palpable untruths, saying my husband put Jollop and such-like in his pills and to prove these statements she publishes his receit, which shows they consisted of the best Tartar, Saltpeter, heated together in an iron kettle, stirred well and allowed to cool. This salt is then mixed with Oyl of Turpentine and stirred, and allowed to stand for six months, then opium and hellebire added, the whole being then well beaten into a paste with a little more turpentine." This she declares was the true receipt for the " Famous Pills " made by Richard Mathews.

After the widow's death, the pill business was carried on by " James Monk of the *Three Neats Tongues* in Bull and Mouth-street at Butcher-Hall Lane end." According to his bill, the pills had been made there for thirty years by the late widow, " who imparted her secret only to my wife, her Grand-daughter, who assisted her for many years.

" This pill being composed of simples of a very power-full operation, extracted from their churlish and malignant quality by long preparation, is by it made amicable to nature."

The dosage forms the quaintest part of the bill, thus the ordinary dose for men or women is " the bigness of a great gray pea ; to children of two years old, the quantity of a barley corn and to them newly-born, the littleness of a pin's head."

It is evident from a bill issued by J. Sintelaer, who exploited the " Royal Decoction," that he was a firm believer in his own nostrum, for he offers to enter into an engagement from £100 to £500 for the performance of his promises, which are as follows : " If any patient whatsoever, tho' left off by all other Physicians and Surgeons and salivated ten or twelve times, will come to his House, where they shall be furnished with all necessaries, as well as physick, for the space of eight days, in which time if they are not so miraculously recovered as not to doubt of a perfect cure within thirty days limit, they are free to return to their own homes, without giving him a penny either for Lodging, Diet or his Physick, which fair proposal is sufficient to convince the world he is no Impostor. The Doctor or his wife are to be spoken with at his house (late the Duke of Leeds) over against the *Red Bull Inn*, near Little Turnstile in Holbourn."

" No Pocky Bill," is the heading of a sheet issued by a quack and his wife who lived at the next house to the

Green Dragon on the right-hand side of Scroop's Court, upon the Freestones, over against St. Andrew's Church in Holbourn.

Their remedy was the " Most pleasing, easie and agreeable Cathartick Potion, having no smell nor taste, but LIKE THAT OF BRANDY, which is but 2s. 6d. a bottle. They have likewise such remedies for any cancerated breast, without any maner of Butcherey or Ruff means us'd, which the world affords not the like."

" A New Dispensary to save Patient's money and the Publick health," was the name given to a company of quacks who thus sought to combat the institution in Warwick Lane established by the College of Physicians.

" This Dispensary," they announce, " is not set on Foot by a Society of Physicians, but is where instead of large Fees, long Bills and Quacks more dangerous practice, all persons, in what circumstances whatsoever that are curable by physick, may be undertaken and managed, with as much safety and judgment and integrity, as if they had the advice of a whole Colledge, but with much less expense than the meanest pretender. For which purpose the Society have provided a Collection of the Choicest Specificks yet known, which we call our SECRET CABINET adapted to all diseases. Therefore be it known, we have always ready, The 'Green Cathartick Elixir,' far exceeding any other for gripes and cholick; The 'Hysterical Tincture'; The 'Great Balsamick Spirit'; The 'White Cardialgick Powder', which in all cases excels Crab's eyes, Pearl, Coral and all the Testaceous Powders; The

' Grey Ointment ' and ' The Black Cerecloth ' or Plaister
for the Rickets call'd ' The Jewel,' a secret left by a
Famous Jew, who got a vast estate by it, which since
his death has been communicated to one of the Society
as the most valuable thing in the World for all wounds.

"Note. The Society have taken care to provide particular specificks for all the *modish diseases*."

Another new departure in quackery, was the introduction of a nostrum through the medium of a lecture
on a curious subject, and thus the maker of the "Electuarium Mirable " sought to attract attention to his
remedy. He announces in a bill addressed to " All
curious Gentlemen, Physicians and others, who shall
think themselves concern'd, that on Thursday the 28th
of this instant July, will be read at Stationer's Hall, a
Lecture of ' Anatomy on the Caul and its use in infants ' ;
wherein it will be plainly proved, that that membrane
in brutes vulgarly called the Leaf and by Physicians the
Caul, is generally consum'd or wasted away in newly
born children that die afterwards of gripes and convulsions, which proceed from this Tabes Omentalis or
Consumption of the Caul ; and further, it will hereby
be manifested that the want of that Part is the real
cause that this disease becomes so universally mortal,
and is now grown as it were Epidemical in London.

" The Author designs to satisfie the Publick at once
in the Truth of this discovery by Evident Demonstration, and he has delivered out Tickets at a guinea each,
to be had at White's Chocolate-House and the Smyrna
Coffee-house near St. James', Tom's Coffee-house in
Covent Garden and Batson's Coffee-house in Corn-hill."

He concludes by announcing that his " Electuarium Mirable " may be had at the *Golden Ball* in Princes-street, near Stocks Market.

The " New Worlds Water," was the name given to a " Wonderful Secret not known in all the three parts of our Continent, but only by the " Gentleman " that prepareth it himself. Lived 20 years in that Misery when by the Great mercy of God, he met in one part of America with a native of Mexico, who cured him with this water. And it happening that the Plague did rage there, his dear Physician died in his house. But before his death he presented him with this Precious Secret saying, he valued it above all the riches of his country. It is to be had only at Mr. William Chandler's between the *Goat-Ale-House* and the *Crown,* over against *Sergeant's-Inn* in Chancery lane."

CHAPTER XVI

AN ELIXIR FOR RENEWING YOUTH—OLD QUACK MEDICINES

MOSES Stringer, a well-known London quack who flourished at the end of the XVIIth century, claimed to have discovered a cure for Old Age which he called "Elixir Renovans." He chose an ingenious method of advertising both himself and his nostrum, in the form of letters which he addressed to the "Learned Dr. Woodrofe, Master of Worcester College in Oxford."

These effusions he had printed and distributed as bills. The first reads as follows :

" Sir,
" Since I had the honour of your Instructions in the University concerning physick and chemistry, I have in a particular manner, apply'd myself to the study of those sciences. I have considered the nature of Humane Bodies and consulted the History of the Ancients, tho' I can't give credit to what the Poets record of Æson ; yet, what Paracelsus reports concerning the force of medicines in Recovering Old Age, affects me very much.

"That Learned Chymist made his first experiment upon a Hen, so very old, that nobody would kill it, either out of a sense of profit or good-nature. He mingled some of his medicine, which he called Renovating Quintessence, with a quantity of Barly and gave it to the Hen, fifteen days together. The effects were wonderful, and the Hen recovered Youth and New Feathers, and what is still more surprising, LAID EGGS and Hatcht chickens as if she had lost a dozen years of her age.

"But this small experiment in Animals did not content the inquisitions of that Scrutinous Chymist, who turned his skill to the relief of mankind. An ancient woman that kept his house, with the consequences of Old Age, was upon the very margin of Death. He gave her the same medicine, fifteen days together, as he had prescribed to his feathered patient and the success was the same. She recover'd her Health, Youth, Hair and Teeth again. Her complexion lookt florid and vigorous, and Nature exerted itself as it generally does in Young Women.

"Reflecting upon these Cures, and the probity and candor of the Physician from whence they proceeded, I thought such a remedy might be formed as might renew youth very much and help Old Age.

"Some years since, with considerable cost and pains, I had the good fortune to find out two medicines of general use, the ' Elixir Febrifugum Martis ' and ' Salt of Lymons,' but finding (tho' the cures effected by them were surprising) yet they did not extend to renew Age so much as I could have wish't, I therefore, a second time, endeavoured and I hope have found, a Medicine which very much lessens the Infirmities of Age, renders Nature vigorous and Stretches the Span of Human Life as far as Heaven permits.

"'THE SAME MEDICINE CURES THE GOUT.'

"Sir,

"I am sensible that this letter proves very long, and I shall take another time to acquaint you with anything remarkable that shall occur to the knowledge of, Sir,

"Your most Humble and Faithful Friend

Moses Stringer."

In a second letter, Stringer has more to say of his discovery and the cures he has performed with his remedy.

"Sir,

"My method of curing Old Age and the Gout is thus, I prescribe them, these drops, which are called 'Elixir Renovans, quia a fatigatione renovat,' because it doth refresh them and make them young again. And to be had only at my House, for fear of Counterfeits, at a Guinea a Bottle, sealed with Three Eagles displayed.

"To be taken from 15 drops to 60 at a time, four or five times a day in Wine, Ale, Beer or Water or in other proper Infusion."

He describes the wonderful effects of the Elixir in a note in which he relates, how he "first cured his Mother, who was extremely swelled with the Dropsie, having born eleven children, and was given over by the physicians." Then he cured his "Wife's Father who had his arm Palsy-struck."

"Another remarkable case was the cure of one who

had been a slave in Algiers in the year 1678, and by the ill-usage he had received, had a Fever and Calenture, Scurvy, Dropsie and Palsy, one succeeding another. He was near 55, and continued a year in St. Thomas's Hospital but could find no remedy. In this wretched condition he languished 20 years, until he took my ' Renovating Elixir ' and he is now absolutely recovered, and more plump and fat than ever he was in his life. His name is Philip Becket, late Commander of a Merchantman, and lives in Shadwell Parish near the Market, where all curious persons may be satisfied of the truth of these occurrences."

The fact that his death was prematurely announced by a rival, led Stringer to issue another bill from his House in Black Fryers, near Puddle-Dock, in which he states: "The Spreading Error that Sir Moses Stringer (commonly call'd Dr. Stringer) Her Majesties Chymist and Mineral-Master-General is Dead, was occasioned by the death of Dr. Salmon in Black Fryers.

"Dr. Stringer *yet remains in Health* (thanks be to God) to execute his office, and finds time to prepare his Secret Chymical, Mineral, Medicines as hereto-fore, which are sold at his Laboratory in the Mineral Office Royal in Black Fryers, with a book of ample directions."

"Beware of Quacks, Mercury and all such Foes
Lest need ye require a supplemental Nose !

is the warning of a quack who lived in Plough Yard in Fetter-lane, at the *Green Door and two Golden Spikes.*

" For the real good of the Publick he is willing to give his advice in all diseases gratis, and claims that his medicines will restore a good temperature of body, whereby perfect health may be gained to the Prolongation of Life and Felicity of a most healthful Constitution without salivation, danger of mercury or confinement, and for less charge and in less time and fewer doses, than is usual for the perfection of a cure."

From early times linseed has had a reputation as a domestic remedy for coughs and colds, but J. L. who frequented Batson's Coffee-house near Change time, claims to have been the first to sell the oil for use as an internal remedy.   According to his bill, " The Right, New, Cold-Drawn Linseed-Oyl, which is so famous for the distempers, phthisick, colds, and the only remedy for the Plurisie, is drawn by J. L., being the first author who put the same Oyl to be sold, at first at the Rainbow Coffee-house by Fleet street, but is now sold at Mr. Batson's and at Sam's Coffee-house by the Custom House, and Say's on Ludgate Hill, at Two shillings a pint bottle."

Another remedy called the " British Oyl " and the " Strong Rock Oyl " was sold by Mrs. Moreton at the *Blew Bodice* in the Long-walk near Christchurch Hospital, which she extolled for its virtues in healing Contusions, Bruises, Rheumatism, Gout, King's Evil and Broken Bones.

It was to be taken inwardly in doses of 50 to 60 drops in wine, ale, or sugar and was recommended as a good antidote against poisons.   According to Mrs. Moreton, " Madamoiselle, Daughter of the Marquis of Harcourt

in Kensington Square, was cured of a rheumatick pain
in her stomack by bathing the same with this oyl."

The " Electuary of Balm of Gilead " and likewise the
" Salt of the Balm of Gilead " were sold by one John
Gray at the *Golden Head* on the *Balcony*, betwixt Craven
House and the *Three Bowls*, in Drury-lane. " These
two of the Famousest medicines in the world, by the
blessing of God, cure Fevers of all kinds, rheumatisms,
dropsie, cholick and consumptions. It is a very good
medicine to carry to the East and West Indies, for it
cures the distempers of the country, likewise all that
travel by land or water, as it is good for any green wound
bruise, scald or any inward distemper in men, women
or children."

A quack who " returned to his lodgings at the house of
Mr. Gwins, a Cloath-worker, in Little Trinity-lane, near
Queen-Hithe, after his travels," thus addresses his
friends : " After my Travels, the Lord hath been pleased
to bring me safe to this former place of my habitation ;
He hath also been good unto me to answer me that, in
that I have sought after, and as He hath given to me
many large talents. I desire with the assistance of Him
to put them forth to the best use for the good of the
world, that when my Lord cometh to inquire of me
what use I have made, He may find them doubled,
and then will He say, ' Well done good and faithful
servant.'

" If any be diseased let them repair to me and I
shall be free in my advice or direction to all for the
Lord hath called and I must hear. When the poor cry

shall I stop my ears ?   No, God forbid, the poor of the
World are Rich in God.

"I will not be like the physitians of the times.   Look
into the 5th chapter of Jeremiah, verse 28, that agrees
with them.   If any of the world be troubled or offended
at my good will to all, let me satisfie them with the wise
sayings of Solomon.   Proverbs 3 chap. 32 verse. ' For
the froward is abomination to the Lord, but his secrets
is with the righteous.'

"As the Lord hath given me a Healing Hand, I am
willing to employ it with thankfulness.   Farewell.
SOLI DEO GLORIA."

An interesting foreshadowing of the cause of a disease
comes to light in a bill emanating from "A Physitian at
the *New-House* in the *Wash Garden*, in Haydon Yard in
the Little Minories."   In it he states, that by his "Studies
he hath experimentally Attained to the Perfect and
Speedy Cure of the Pox, his medicines being of such an
efficacious quality that they totally eradicate all venerial
Atomes, which infect and vitiate the blood, extracting
the malignity although it be settled in the Bones."

Another cure for ague, with special reference to Kent,
was advertised by a quack who lived in "White-cross
street in Cripple-gate Parish, almost at the further end
near Old Street, turning in by the sign of the *Black
Crow* in *Goat Alley*, straight forward *down three steps*
at the sign of the *Globe*, where he hath dwelt almost
Twenty years.   He hath a Cure for an Ague, either in
man, woman or child in London or in Kent, which never
yet failed, at once or three times taking.   Either liquor,
pill or powder, the dose no bigger than a Pin's head, it

hath neither smell nor tast and the price of each dose is one shilling."

One of the most popular proprietary remedies of the XVIIth century was Elixir Salutis or Daffy's Elixir, which is said to have been originated by the Rev. Thomas Daffy the rector of Redmile about 1660.

In a bill issued by his daughter Katherine Daffy, who carried on its manufacture after his death, she states : " It is prepared by me from the best druggs according to Art and the original receipt which my Father the Rev. Thomas Daffy, late Rector of Redmile in the Valley of Belvoir, imparted to his kinsman Mr. Anthony Daffy, who published the same to the benefit of the community.

" The very original Receipt is now in my possession, left to me by my father. My own brother, Mr. Daniel Daffy, formerly Apothecary in Nottingham made this Elixir from the same receipt, and sold it there during his life. Those who know me will believe what I declare.

" The true Elixir is sold at the *Hand and Pen* in Maiden-lane, Covent Garden and at many Coffee-houses, also at Mr. John Waters, Perfumer at the *Naked Boy and Orange Tree*, near the Maypole in the Strand."

There were several makers of this remedy and among them was "John Harrison of Prujeans Court in the Old Baily, who in 1709, charged Mrs. Elizabeth Daffy with making Invidious remarks upon his Elixir Salutis." She charged him, with taking the "House in Prujeans Court Clandestinly and with pretending to be her husband's assistant in preparing the Elixir." Harrison on his part declared, that " he knew the secret sometime before the death of his father, Dr. Anthony Daffy, which he presumes was before the said Elias Daffy was privy to the preparing of the said Elixir (he being then a Cambridge scholar) and the same was communicated to him in the year 1684, at the time when he was going to travel beyond the sea."

Harrison, after denying Mrs. Daffy's allegations concludes, " I am well assured that those who have tried mine will apply themselves to nobody else for Elixir Salutis."

Daffy's Elixir is said to have been composed of Senna, Jalap, Aniseed, Caraway seeds and Juniper berries, macerated in alcohol, to which treacle and water were afterwards added.

It is still sold in London and the bills wrapped round the bottle state that, " The Elixir was much recommended to the public by Dr. King, Physician to King Charles II, and the late learned and ingenious Dr. Radcliffe."

Another early patent medicine that attained great popularity in the XVIIth century, especially in Scotland and France, were Anderson's Scots Pills.

Their originator was Dr. Patrick Anderson, a well-known physician of the Stuart period, who in 1635, published a treatise on his pills, the recipe for which he says he obtained in Venice.

After his death, they were made and sold by his daughter, Katherine Anderson, and she by deed, in 1686, transferred the secret to Thomas Weir a surgeon of Edinburgh, who obtained a patent for their preparation in 1687.

A few years later, the formula came into the hands
of Mrs. Isabella Inglish who declares in a bill, that she
was authorised by their Majesties, to prepare and
publish them at the *Hand and Pen* near the King's
Bagnio in Long Acre.

There were apparently rival preparations in the field
for Mrs. Inglish states that, "she alone makes Dr.
Anderson's Grana Angelica or the famous true Scots
Pills and no others are genuine."

She stigmatises in particular one Mogson, whom she
says by his advertisements, "pretends to have the
Receipt from Mrs. Katherine Anderson as being intimately acquainted with her in Scotland, and hath
had the impudence to counterfeit my printed directions
verbatim.

"Nor can he make appear he was ever in Scotland
as he falsely pretends," she continues, "Nay, so little
truth is in his assertions, that in March last, he himself
did meet with me at Mr. Lloyd's Coffee-house in Lom-
bard street, and desired him to vend my pills there, but
since then he hath trick'd him and me both, which can
and may perhaps be made appear in as publick a manner, as he hath made himself a Lyar to the view of the
world. I offer to prove out of all doubt, as I have
already done before the King's Physicians, that the
said Mogson discovered the cheat himself on the 16th
day of September last to two gentlemen, to whom he
pretended that he was intimately acquainted with Dr.
Anderson at Edinburgh, who admitted him into his
closet whence he stole the said Receipt out of a book of
the Doctor's; whereas the said Doctor has been dead

above fifty years, being long before Mogson was born."

John Gray of the *Golden Head*, between the Little Turnstile and the *Bull Inn* in High Hobourn, also claimed to make the pills " according to the doctor's method during his life-time " and sold them at 5s. a box in 1699.

Gray sealed his boxes with his coat of arms in red wax with his motto " Remember you must die " wrapped round them, and still another claimant named Man, made and sold the *true Pills* at " Old Man's Coffee-house " at Charing Cross in 1703.

Anderson's Scots Pills are said to have been composed of Aloes, Jalap and Oil of Aniseed and are still made and sold in London.

Mr. Lewis of the *Blew Ball* in Little Bridges street and Russell street, Covent Garden, sold a number of these old quack medicines, and in a bill he issued in 1711, declares the Dr. Anderson's Scots pills, " are the nicest thing in the World to sweeten, purifie, and cleanse the blood and of great use to Sea-men, Travellers and Fast-Livers."

He also sold Daffy's Elixir Salutis, " richly prepared with Venice Treacle, the greatest preservative that art or nature can suggest."

He was the maker of the " True Friars Balsam, suffi-ciently known to the Nobility and Gentry, which has gained the reputation of the greatest Balsamick in the world. 'Twas never published 'till now, but has been kept by the Gentry, who were at the expence of making it as a Closet Jewel. Sold in Flint bottles at 10s. each."

Lewis also sold a "Comforting Stomack Plaister for coughs, colds and wheesings. 'Tis worn by several persons as a Stomacher all the winter for a preservative." He further warranted that his "Ague and Intermitting Fever powder had no Jesuit's Powder in it."

Another Apothecary who billed his own medicines, was Robert Rotheram of the *Golden Ball* in Sweetings Alley, in Corn hill, near the Royal Exchange, in 1678.

Rotheram made an Elixir of Saffron, "a great Cordial," which he claimed would "expel Poyson, cure feavors and wonderfully inlive Nature." He also sold an "Elixir of Balme and Mint," which he declared would "quicken all the faculties of Nature, make a cheerful heart and a lively countenance; each glass being sealed with the Bleeding Pelican."

John Coniers, an apothecary who lived in Shoe Lane and afterwards at ye *White Lyon* in Fleet street, appears to have been the first to sell an artificial mineral water. In a bill dated May 12th 1679, he states that, he prepares and sells "An essence made of ye Minerall which quicklie you can make Tunbridge Waters. Any soft spring water mixt with a little thereof, becomes in nature a True Tunbridge Water of great use to those who desired to be spared ye journey to ye Wells.

"Mixt with Tunbridge Water itselfe, makes it so much stronger as you please. A great advantage to those, especially who cannot beare much mixt with Epsom or other purging waters, makes it ye nature of Astrop Waters."

Coniers was an interesting man and had a Museum which he had "collected with much assiduity and at great expense," and in 1691 made a proposal to open it to the public for general inspection.

Snuff, like tobacco, was originally recommended as a medicinal agent, and among those who first exploited it was Edwyn Salter, who introduced a "Sternutatory Snuff" to "fortify the brain and its animal faculties." It was sold at the house next door to the *Sugar loaf* in Nevill's Alley, Fetter-lane.

"Lisbon Snuff, strongly recommended to improve the eyesight," was sold by Mr. Harrison at the West End of the Royal Exchange, at 23s. a pound or 6s. an ounce.

Snuff was also used as a remedy for toothache, and for that purpose there was the "best Orangare, fine Burgamot, Tongcar, Germany and Itallian snuffs at 2s. and 1s. an ounce. The best Spanish, Havana and Sevile Snuffs were sold at 5s. a pound," and any of these are recommended in a bill dated 1706, "as a present remedy for the *most violentest Headache* or *Toothache*, and as infallible curers of *Coughs* or *Ptsicks*, and a preventer of those distempers."

Jatropoton was the name given to a liquid or powder for adding to Wines, Beers, Cyders or other drinks, "as a corrective of all noxious aigre or that were too sharp, sour or flat, that was sold by Mr. Walford at John's Coffee-house in Birchin lane, near the Royal Exchange. "By a few drops of the Liquor or Salt, in an instant, the drink retaining its full taste, vertue and colour, except that it renders all such too sharp, and flat drink softer and brisker, to any degree required. All Rhenish wines without the Clary flavour, seem converted into perfect

Burgundy. In wines mixt with water, it has the full effect of the German Spaws.

" This liquor or salt is an Occult Alcali that is to taste perfectly saline, and is qualified to penetrate and pass deep into the Digestions and must of necessity absorb and dulcify all noxious acids, and dissolve all preternatural coagulations there as in a glass vial.

" It will dulcify the strongest hard cheese, instantly qualifies for digestion, as it was used by the Romans after a late Debauch or Surfeit."

There were several quacks who advertised to treat ruptures and prominent among them was Bartlett of Goodmans-fields, who was one of the oldest makers of "Spring Trusses, Collars, Swings and other inventions."

In his bill, he claims to be able to cure " men from forty to seventy nine of this malady, and reduce desperate Ruptures in a few minutes, likely to be mortal in a few hours. I can make the weak strong, and the crooked straight." Bartlett carried on his business at the *Golden*

Ball by the Tavern in Prescot street, and at the *Golden Ball and Naked Boys*, against the Rainbow Coffee-house.

Another orthopædic quack named Nathaniel Baker, who lived at the *Golden Spurr* in Round Court in St. Martin's-Legrand, near Newgate street, informs the public that, he has "lately come to England (by the Help of God) and undertakes to set all children straight that are growing awry, either in body, legs, or feet.

" It has been my business," he states, " for upwards of thirty years having perfected the cure of some hundreds, who for want of timely application, would have been deformed and cripples all days of their lives ; the sooner I am applied to the better. I do it without putting to any pain."

CHAPTER XVII

UNTIL the close of the XVIIth century, baths were practically unknown in the palace or private house. It was not until about 1679, that the public bagnios or sweating houses began to be established in London, on the lines of the Hummums, which had been common in Turkey and the near East from an early period.

One of the first to be opened was the Duke's Bagnio and Bath in Salisbury Stables, Long Acre, for which Sir William Jennings in 1679, procured his Majesty's patent "for making all public bagnios and baths, either for sweating, bathing or washing."

An interesting description of this establishment from which we can picture the Bagnio of the period, is given in a bill issued at the time of the opening and reads as follows:

" Entering the Hall, where the porter stands to take the money, you pass into a room furnished with a pair of scales, and thence into the dressing room with private boxes on each side, the middle walk of which is paved with black and white marble. This room is moderately warm. Then you pass into the bagnio, over which is a cupula supported by eight stone pillars within which you walk. This is paved with marble, the sides lined with white gally-tiles, and in the walls are ten seats as in the baths at Bath, and nitches, holding marble basins for washing.

" On one side hangs a very handsome pendulum clock to tell exactly how the time passes. Adjoining, are four little round rooms, each about eight feet in size, of various temperatures and in each is a leaden cistern or bath, six feet long by Two feet wide.

" The visitor is received by the barbers in the dressing room and later a rubber brings him wooden clogs in exchange for slippers. He may then lounge or walk, or take a bottle of ' diaphoretick liquor.'

" After about an hour, his rubber dry-rubs him with a hair-chamolet glove, then having filled a cistern (bath) the patient lies in it, the water being gradually made colder."

At the Duke's Bagnio, four days a week were allotted for men and two days reserved for women only. The large bath was in a separate apartment, which was filled with water impregnated with salt. It measured ten feet long, seven feet broad and was five feet deep.

At the Royal Bagnio in Newgate street, the charge was four shillings for each person, and the bill goes on to state, " there is lately found out a good and clear water for bathing, and any persons that have no mind to sweat, may be cup'd either the old way or according to the modern invention for 2s. 6d."

It was a common practice, when bleeding was so much in vogue to be " cupped " at the baths where a cupper was generally in attendance as at the Thermæ of ancient Rome. He had a regular trade and usually carried his instruments with him for performing the wet or dry operation, which was then believed to be beneficial to health. His apparatus comprised a set of glass or metal cups, a spirit lamp and a lancet. By the method generally employed, the air was first exhausted from one of the cups by means of the lighted lamp, or a piece of wool soaked in spirit, and after an incision was made with the lancet the cup was pressed over the spot to receive the blood. The dry method was carried out by means of a spring scarificator, an instrument with six or more sharp blades which were released on pressing a trigger. This instrument, which was invented towards the end of the XVIIth century, consisted of a metal box in which the blades were concealed, it was pressed close to the skin and when the blades were released by pressing the trigger, they penetrated the skin about the eighth of an inch.

The Queen's Bagnio in Long Acre, was kept by a surgeon named Henry Ayme, who states in a bill he issued in 1706, " The Queen's Bagnio is lately beautified and divided into several rooms and is more convenient than before for the reception of both sexes, where they may sweat and bathe every day in the week and be private to themselves.

" This Bagnio is well known for to exceed all others, and to be more frequented by the Nobility and Gentry, by reason there is added a lesser Bagnio of a lower rate for the Diseased and meaner sort.

" Those that desire, may be Bath'd without sweating,

either in cold or hot bath, and cupt after the newest and easiest way with an instrument that scarifies all at once, with little or no pain, being the best of that kind ever yet invented. The price for one single person is five shillings, but if two or more come together, four shillings each.

"There is no entertainment for women after twelve of the clock at night, but all gentlemen that desire beds, may have them for two shillings a night for one single person, but if two lie together, three shillings both; which Rooms and Beds are fit for the entertainment of persons of the highest quality."

The Hummums in Brownlow street, Drury-lane was kept by John Evans, where he says, "persons may sweat to what degree they please." There were several apartments with varying degrees of heat, where "private sweating, bathing and fine cupping, after the new German manner were performed with greater ease than ever yet known with good and clean linnen."

The Germans employed a small spring fleam for cupping with a single lancet-shaped blade which on being released, penetrated the vein it was desired to open.

Evans informs his customers, that he has "a diligent attendance of both sexes attending every day. Likewise he had good conveniences for cold bathing, which was highly approved of all persons.

"The price for one person alone is three shillings, two persons together five shillings. Every person that comes single, hath a private apartment to him or herself.

It is also accommodated with good lodgings for such as desire to Lie all night.

" If any persons desires to be Cupt at their chambers, he will wait on them." He particularly warns visitors that there are *Two Spikes* before the door, to prevent mistakes.

A Sweating House was kept at the sign of the *Black Prince* in Duck-lane near West Smithfield, " where all persons of both sexes may be sweated every Tuesday, Wednesday, Friday and Saturday, without fail. The Prices for men and women is one shilling and sixpence and those that are cupp'd the whole charge will be two shillings.

"There is likewise a back door that comes into Bartholomew Close between the *Chequer* and the *Red Ball* where you will see over the door *The Sweating and Cupping House.*"

There was another Bagnio or Sweating house in the Old Bailey next door to the sign of the *Black Bull*, " where both men and women may be well accommodated at convenient seasons, being three days for men and three days for women."

The bill states that " Sweating is as useful as Bathing. It eases pains in the limbs, opens the pores of the Body, evacuates superfluous Humours, cleanses the blood, prevents and cures the scurvy, and is most excellent in expelling those infectious and venomous humours, and 'tis the best antidote in the world against all contagious distempers.

" In the same house there is a Bath, for such as desire it, upon timely notice given, and this shall be artificially composed according as the necessity of the patients distemper requires.   Probatum bonum."

The card of Wilcox, the Cupper at the Royal Bagnio informs the public that, "he now liveth at the *Turk's Head* in Newgate street over against Butcher-Hall-lane where he hath very good conveniences for sweating, bathing, shaving and cupping after the best manner."

The China Hummum was kept by P. Brook in New Red-Lyon-Street in Holborn, against great Turnstile.

'THE TURK'S HEAD'
From the card of Wilcox the Cupper

Here he says he carries on " sweating and bathing both at once, after the China Manner by a "Dew Bath" without entering into water or heat of fire, or breathing the air wherein the body sweats. This is only performed by the heat and moisture of a continued warm vaporous Dew or Steam arising from Decoctions of all sorts of Drugs, as Herbs, flowers, seeds, woods, waters, wines, etc., of various properties and qualities according to each one's occasion, which continually flowing and distilling on the body during all the time and is always prepared anew peculiarly for every one that uses it.

" The Physicians Arms are over the door."

Cupping was also carried on by women, and we learn from a bill that, " At Canbury Cold Bath at Islington, Mary Lucas ' cups ' Ladies at Home and abroad whenever required. She hopes those ladies she has had the Honour to guide at the late Mr. Jones's Cold Bath in Newgate-street, will be pleased to employ her, and that those who have since honoured her with their favours, will continue the same."

Lacy's Bagnio in Leicester Fields, was the scene of the final episode in the career of that extraordinary impostor Mary Toft, the " rabbit-breeding woman of Godliman," and where she made a full confession of the fraud which had deceived some of the most distinguished medical men of the time.

Among the frequenters of the Bagnios were the chiropodists or corn-cutters, many of whom came from Holland where the practice of their art was more common than in England.

One of the best known was Thomas Smith of King street, Westminster, who describes himself, as the " first Master Corn-cutter of England." He states in his bill, that he " learnt the art of taking out and curing all manner of corns without pain or drawing of blood, by experience and ingenuity in a way no man in England can do the like.

" I wear a silver badge with three verses, the first in English, the second in Dutch and the last in French,

with the States General of Holland for the many cures
I there did and many more in London, by several persons
of quality and others which are too tedious here to
relate, and my name on the Badge underwritten, Thomas
Smith, who will not fail (God willing) to make out every
particular in this bill."

Smith appears to have been ubiquitous and periodi-
cally visited all the best known Coffee-houses in town.
He says, " I am to be spoken with till 8 in the morning
and at 6 at night at Home, and every day at these
Coffee-houses following, morning and evening.   The
' Rainbow' at Fleet-bridge and at Richards, Nandos,
Temple, Mannaring's, ' The Grecian' and Brown's, all
in Fleet-street near the Temple.   From 1 to 4, at
Grigby's in Threadneedle-street, the backside of the
Royal Exchange, or at the Lisbon Coffee-house next
door and at the Amsterdam Coffee-house, the London
Coffee-house by the Antwerp Tavern, and each evening
going home, I call at all the Coffee-houses above Toms
and Wills near Covent Garden, Squire's in Fuller's
Rents, Holborne, Ormonde-street at Mr. Man's, the
Royal Coffee-house near Whitehall, Mrs. Wells under
Scotland-Yard gate, Alice's, Waghorn's, and all the
Parliament Coffee-houses all adjoining to the Parliament
House, where I am ready to serve any Gentlemen or
Lady."

Another corn-curer was Thomas Shadells, who lived
in Sea-Coal-lane in Bear Alley near the Old Bailey.   He
declares that, " he hath an infallible remedy to cure
corns so that they will never grow or offend again,
putting a drop of falling spittle upon a thin bit of

leather, and then two drops out of the bottle, every morning till the bottle is out. He has likewise a ball for the bottoms of the feet, putting it on a plaster every week till cured. He sells it for 3d. at delivery and 3d. when cured. Enquire at the Glover's shop under Ludgate, and there you may be informed of him, otherwise you may have them at the *Black Lyon* in Cree-lane. I also cut corns to all Gentlemen's satisfaction. I have a green plaister for a hard corn and a white plaister for a soft corn, both of them 1d."

Both tea and coffee, when first introduced into England, were originally recommended for their remedial properties.

The first Coffee-house opened in London was established by Pasqua Rosee, a Ragusan, in St. Michael's-Alley, Corn-hill in 1652. He issued a bill describing the "Vertue of the Coffee Drink. First made and publickly sold in England by Pasqua Rosee."

In this he describes how the berries should be dried in an oven, then ground to powder and boiled up with spring water, half a pint to be drunk an hour before eating.

"It is a very good help to digestion, quickens the spirits and is *good against sore eyes. Is good against headache, helpeth consumptions* and the *cough of the lungs.* It is also excellent to prevent *dropsy, gout* and *scurvy,* and will prevent *drowsiness* and make one fit for business. It is made and sold in St. Michael's-Alley in Corn-hill by Pasqua Rosee, at the *Sign of his own head.*"

Thus coffee, which soon became a favourite beverage, was first recommended for its medicinal virtues.

It was at Garraway's Coffee-house, that tea was first sold as " a cure for all disorders," at 16s. to 50s. a pound. Tea drinking was originally introduced into Europe by the Dutch in the early part of the XVIIth century, and it was not until after 1650 it first began to be used in England. The earliest known advertisement concerning it appeared in the " Mercurius Politicus " in 1658, in which it is alluded to as, that " Excellent and by all physitians approved Chinese drink called Tcha, by other nations Tay or Tee sold at *Sultaners Head* Cophee-house in Sweeting's-Rents by the Royal Exchange."

" The Volatile Spirit of Bohee-Tea " is the subject of a bill that was issued shortly afterwards, in which it is recommended as " the most absolute *cure for consumptions*, and all other decays of Nature whatsoever incident to mankind ; being infinitely more Balsamick and healing to the Lungs than the common Infusion of the leaf in water.

" It is likewise a very rich cordial for *clearing the heart* when oppress'd with *melancholy and Vapours*.

" This spirit, the first of its kind that was ever made in England, mix'd with Punch makes one of the most agreeable liquors in the world.

" It is also a special Antidote against *any Infection of the Air* and if 15 drops be taken going to bed in a glass of spring water, it never faileth to procure a sound sleep. It is sold at 2s. 6d. a bottle at Batson's Coffee-house against the Royal Exchange and at no other place."

Mr. Lattese, a Piedmontese gentleman, astonished the Town by an advertisement, concerning what he claims to be, an " Extraordinary Discovery." He states, that by "a long course of experiments, he has discovered the wonderful secret of procreating either sex at the joint option of the parents. Should they desire to have a daughter, the success cannot be warranted with absolute certainty, but should they concur in their wishes to have a son, they may rely that by strictly conforming to a few easy and natural directions, they will positively have a boy."

This had not failed in a single instance during 16 years that this SECRET ARCANUM had been known to him.

"As to conditions and terms," he continues, "these must in a great measure depend on circumstances to be considered and settled at an interview, but to prevent trouble and fruitless applications, Mr. Lattese thinks fit to premise, that he will pay no attention but to letters post paid and signed with real names, directed to him at the Antigallican Coffee-house by the Royal Exchange."

Nothing more is known of Mr. Lattese's discovery and he fails to produce any testimonials as to its success.

Contraceptives were not unknown in the XVIIth century and Colonel Condum, who lived in the reign of Charles II, is credited with their invention.

They were originally made from the dried gut of a sheep and were first sold at two taverns near Covent Garden viz., the *Rummer* and the *Rose*, the latter hostelry in Russell-street, being a famous meeting place in Stuart times.

They were afterwards made and sold by Mrs. Philips at the *Green Canister* in Half-Moon-street, near the

Strand, who is said to have made a fortune from her business and retired.

From a bill issued some years afterwards, Mrs. Philips announces, that " after ten years leaving off business, she had been prevailed on by her friends to re-assume the same, and she has taken a house at No. 5 Orange Court near Leicester Fields. To prevent mistakes, over the door is the sign of the *Golden Fan* and *Rising Sun*, a lamp adjoining the sign, and fan-mounts in the window."

She defies anyone in England to equal her goods, as she has had 35 years experience in the business of making and selling these " implements of safety." She has likewise a great choice of skins and bladders for apothecaries, chymists, and druggists, and also sells all sorts of perfumes.

However, during her retirement, a rival had set up business at the *Green Canister*, and issued a bill stating, that, " the woman who pretended the name of Philips in Orange Court is now dead," and the business is carried on, that has been for forty years at the *Green Canister* in Bedford (late Half-Moon) Street seven doors from the Strand on the left-hand side, " where all gentlemen may be supplied with those bladder policies or implements of safety."

In a significant postscript she adds, " Ambassadors, Foreigners, Gentlemen and Captains of Ships, may be supplied with any quantity."

Mrs. Philips however in another bill indignantly denies that she had departed this life, and states that, " It has been industriously and maliciously reported, that the original Mrs. Philips is dead, which is *entirely false* and without the *least foundation*, as *she can be seen behind the counter, daily.*"

Later on, after her undoubted death, she was succeeded by Mary Perkins at the *Green Canister*, who sold "all sorts of fine machines, otherwise called 'Cundums,' and also washballs, soaps, essences, snuffs, cold cream, lipsalves, sealing wax and ladies black sticking-plaister."

A bill announcing the discovery of the mineral spring discovered at Norwood, thus extols its virtues : " There is lately Found out at Norwood in the Parish of Croyden in the County of Surrey, at Biggen Farm at Richard Jackson's, an excellent Purging Water which hath been approv'd by several eminent Physitians of the Colledge and is found to be one of the best and gentlest Purging Waters that have yet been discovered.

"You may have it at Mr. Timothy Robert's, Fishmonger at the *Cheshire Cheese* in Stock's Market, and at Mr. John Hilliard's at the *Strong Water Shop*, over against Sir Thomas Lane's, near Milk-street Market, London."

CHAPTER XVIII

QUACKS WHO RECEIVED ROYAL PATRONAGE

THE eighteenth century has well been called the golden age of quackery and England the 'Paradise of Quacks,' for they found patrons in all classes of society, from the highest to the lowest.

The bold and unblushing assertions of their never-failing remedies, constantly reiterated by these charlatans always inspired confidence in the sick and ailing.

" Man," says Southey, " is a dupeable animal. Quacks in medicine, quacks in religion and quacks in politics, know this and act upon that knowledge. The credulity of man is unfortunately too strong to resist the impudent assertions of the quack. Credulity has been justly defined as belief without reason. It diffuses itself through the minds of all classes, by which the rank and dignity of science are degraded, and its valuable labours confounded with the vain pretentions of empiricism."

One of the most successful quacks of his time was William Read, who began his career as a jobbing tailor. He was eventually knighted by Queen Anne and became one of the most fashionable practitioners of his day.

He was born in Aberdeen and after forsaking his original calling for the more lucrative trade of quackery, he travelled the country from Yorkshire to Devonshire.

In 1684 he was in Dublin where on March 7th, he issued the following bill:

"Though the Art, experience and reputation of Mr. William Read, practitioner in physick, chyrurgy and a great occulist, be sufficiently known in England and Scotland, where he has long exercised his skill with very good success; yet since he has but lately come into His Majesty's Kingdom of Ireland and has desired our testimonial concerning his performance here. We do certify, that he has done several remarkable cures with great dexterity and success, as the couching of cataracts, cutting off cancerated breasts, mortified arms and legs (and very little effusion of blood by vertue of his excellent Styptic Water) several of which operations, we have with very much satisfaction ourselves seen him perform, as we do testify under our hands and seals the day and year above written.

Signed. Narcissus (Lord Bishop of) Ferns. And. Leighlin. Robert Huntingdon, provost, Allen Mullin, M.D."

On his return to London, he settled in York buildings in the Strand and by persistent advertising, attracted the attention of some influential personages who eventually brought him to the notice of the Queen.

Queen Anne who suffered from a chronic weakness of the eyes, fell an easy victim to the quacks who offered to cure her infirmity. Once having gained her Majesty's favour it proved an easy road to fortune and Read was appointed Oculist-in-Ordinary. He was knighted by the grateful monarch in 1705, it is stated, "on

account of his services to soldiers and seamen for
blindness which he gave gratis."

Inflated by the honour thus bestowed upon him, Read
hired a Grub-street poet to immortalise the great event,
which resulted in the publication of a poem entitled
" The Oculist " in 1705. It began thus :

" Whilst Britain's Sovereign scales such worth has
weighed
And Anne herself her smiling favours paid,
That Sacred hand does your fair chaplet twist,
Great Read her own entitled oculist ! "

Addison says, " Read seems to have been the most
laborious advertiser of his time and the most successful
practitioner in his way. There was an epigram current,
that Sir William could hardly *read*, but he seldom suffered
any periodical to make its appearance in public without
some testimony under his own hand that he could
hardly write.

" It appears he was a very comely person and a man
of fashion, rich and ostentatious. For thirty five years
he had been in the practice of couching cataracts, taking
off all sorts of wens, curing wry-necks and hair-lips,
vending styptick water and a variety of nostrums."
He kept an excellent table and was noted for his special
brew of punch, which he served out to his guests in
golden goblets.

Sir Richard Steele and Nicholas Rowe accepted his
hospitality, but Swift who disliked him and called him a
mountebank, always declined his invitations.

Radcliffe alludes to him as " Read, the mountebank who has assurance enough to come to our table upstairs at Garraways ; swears he'll take his coach and six horses, his two blacks and as many silver trumpets, against a dinner at Pontacks."

After Read and Hannes had been knighted, the following lines appeared :

> " The Queen, like Heav'n, shines equally on all,
> Her favours now without distinction fall,
> Great Read and slender Hannes, both knighted
> show,
> That none their honours shall to merit owe."

Read never lost an opportunity of keeping himself before the public, and after the battle of Malplaquet, he issued the following advertisement on September 11th 1709.

" Sir William Read, Her Majesty's Oculist, being very sensible that many of her Majesty's soldiers must have received damage in their eyes or visive faculty in the late bloody and unparalled battle, thought fit to give public notice for the benefit of all such persons, that he will constantly attend at his house in Durham Yard, where all such persons bringing certificates from their respective officers, shall be kindly received, and all due care taken in order to their speedy cure GRATIS, as it has been his constant practice ever since the beginning of the war."

He was very jealous of anyone practising in his name,

and he trained his wife to assist him, which she did for a considerable time. After the death of Queen Anne, he became sworn-oculist-in-ordinary to King George I, in 1714, but did not long enjoy the office, for he was taken ill and died at Rochester on May 24th 1715.

After his death, his wife carried on the business and issued the following bill :

" The Lady Read in Durham-yard in the Strand, having obtained a peculiar method of couching cataracts and curing all diseases of the eyes, by Sir William Read's method and medicines, and having had above 15 years experience and very great success in curing multitudes of blind and defective in their sight, particularly several who were born blind ; she may be constantly advised with at her house as above, where the poor, Her Majesty's seamen and soldiers may meet with relief gratis.

" Note, Sir William Read has left *only* with his Lady, the *true receipt* of his *Styptick Water*, so famous for stopping all fluxes or effusions of blood and all other of the medicines he frequently used in his practise, which may also be had at the place above mentioned.

" N.B. The Lady Read since the death of Sir William, hath couched several persons and one in particular, who was above 60 years of age, all with very good success and brought them to perfect sight."

Read was succeeded in Royal favour by Roger Grant, who was appointed Sworn-Oculist-in-ordinary to Her Majesty. Grant began life as a tinker and Anabaptist preacher, and gained notoriety by publishing glowing accounts of his cures. He was even more vain than his colleague Read, and delighted to distribute engraved portraits of himself among his friends and patrons.

On one of these a wag wrote :

" A tinker first his scene of life began ;
That falling, he set up for cunning man,
But wanting luck, puts on a new disguise,
And now pretends that he can mend your eyes ;
But this expect, that, like a tinker true,
Where he repairs one eye he puts out two."

He boasted that he could give sight to those born blind and produced testimonials to that effect. His method was to find some poor and illiterate person with imperfect vision, and after treating him with medicines and half-crowns for six weeks, induce him to sign a testimonial to the effect, that he had been born stone-blind and that Dr. Grant had cured him in little more than a month. The way in which he carried out these frauds, is described in a pamphlet published in 1709, entitled " A Full and True Account of a Miraculous Cure of a young man in Newington that was born Blind."

In one bill he states, " Having observed that multitudes of persons, blind and distemper'd in the Eyes have been imposed upon by silly women and such-like ignorant pretenders to the Opthalmick Art, this is therefore to give notice, that at the *Blue Ball* in St. Christopher's Court in Threadneedle-street, behind the Royal Exchange, lives R. Grant, an approved and Sworn-Oculist, whose knowledge in distempers of the eyes has been sufficiently demonstrated, by the many cures he has performed, which are too numerous to be inserted here. He has for many years made the eye of man the only subject of his study and practice, and you are desired to forbear your application to him upon other occasions, for he meddles in nothing but what relates to the Eyes.

" And whereas many persons by Blindness are become a burthen to their Parishes, any such may apply themselves to Mr. Grant with a certificate from the Minister and Church-wardens of their respective parishes, and he will couch them Gratis, as he doth all poor sea-men and soldiers in Her Majesties service."

In his earlier days Grant lived at the *Golden Ball* in Gravel-lane, Southwark, where he sold an " Astringent Sear-Cloth or plaister, good for all sorts of sprains and wrenches. This cloth giveth immediate ease in Gout and prevents it returning with so much violence as formerly, nay, if it not be inveterate gout, it presently cures it, and the price of the Sear-cloth is from one shilling to half-a-crown according to the largeness."

Another quack oculist who achieved considerable notoriety about this period was John Taylor, who styled himself " The Chevalier John Taylor, Ophthalmiator, Pontificial, Imperial, and Royal, who treated Pope Benedict XIV, Augustus III, King of Poland, Frederick V, King of Denmark and Norway and Frederick Adolphus, King of Sweden."

Taylor was a very plausible and cunning charlatan who had a natural gift of speech and a knowledge of several languages. According to Dr. King, " no quack ever appeared with fitter and more excellent talents.

He has a good appearance, a fine hand, good instruments and performs all his operations with great dexterity. He has travelled all over Europe and has always with him an equipage suitable to a man of the first quality, and has been introduced to most of the sovereign princes."

His chief method of advertising was by delivering a lecture on " The Eye," in every place he visited. These harangues were characteristic of quack oratory and full of grandiloquent phrases, as instanced in the one he declaimed to the University of Oxford, which began as follows :

" The eye, most illustrious sons of the muses, most learned Oxonians whose fame I have heard celebrated in all parts of the globe—the eye, that most amazing, that stupendous, that comprehending, that incomprehensible, that miraculous organ the eye, is the Proteus of the passions, the herald of the mind, the interpreter of the heart and the window of the soul. The eye has dominion over all things. The world was made for the eye, and the eye for the world.

" My subject is Light, most illustrious sons of literature—intellectual Light. Ah ! my philosophical, metaphysical, my classical, mathematical, mechanical, my theological, my critical audience, my subject is the eye.

" You are the Eye of England !

" England has two eyes—Oxford and Cambridge. You are the right eye of England, the elder sister in science and the first fountain of learning in all Europe.

" The eye is the husband of the soul !

"The eye is indefatigable. The eye is an angelic faculty. The eye in this respect is a female. The eye is never tired of seeing and enjoying all Nature's vigour."

Taylor was fond of transposing his words in a peculiar manner so as to attract attention, and would sometimes speak of " the eye, on the wonders lecture will I."

On the occasion of his lectures, he generally dressed in black, with a long, light flowing ty'd wig. "He ascended the platform and stood behind a large table covered with a piece of old tapestry, on which was laid a dark coloured cafoy chariot-seat, with four black bunches (as used on hearses) tyed to the corners for tassels. Four large candles were placed on each side of the cushion, and a quart decanter of drinking water, with a half pint glass to moisten his mouth."

Taylor's autobiography, which he published himself, contains some amusing passages. In one part, he declares his allegiance to the " two most amiable ladies this age has produced viz. Lady Inverness and Lady Mackintosh, both the sweetest prattlers, the prettiest reasoners and the best judges of the charms of high life that I ever saw."

He says, " I have lived in many convents of friars of different orders and have been in almost every female nunnery in all Europe (on account of my profession) and could write many volumes on the adventures of these religious beauties. I have been present at the making of nuns of almost every order, and assisted at their religious feasts. I have been present at many extraordinary diversions designed for the amusement of the sovereign viz. the hunting of different sorts of wild beasts, as in Poland, and bull-fighting in Spain.

"I am well acquainted with all the various punishments for different crimes, as practised in every nation, and I am also well instructed in the different ways of giving the torture to extract confessions. I have assisted, and seen the manner of embalming dead bodies of great personages, so all must agree that no man ever had a greater variety of matter worthy to be conveyed to posterity."

Taylor reached the height of his ambition when he was appointed Oculist to King George II, and his son, who called himself John Taylor Junior, who wrote a eulogistic biography of his father, declares that he numbered fifty other Royal personages among his patients.

The son survived the father over fifteen years and carried on a lucrative business as a quack oculist in Hatton Garden. He is described as "an illiterate and cunning scoundrel, without the redeeming qualities which made his parent amusing."

The Chevalier boasting of his knowledge of languages, once challenged Samuel Johnson to talk Latin with him. The Doctor responded with a quotation from Horace, which Taylor took to be "something of his own composition." "He said a few words well enough," Johnson afterwards remarked when relating the story to Boswell. "Taylor is the most ignorant man I ever knew, but sprightly ; Ward the dullest."

Joshua Ward, to whom Johnson refers, was another successful quack who flourished under Royal Patronage in the first half of the XVIIIth century. He was born in 1685 and began his career with his brother, in Thames Street, where they carried on business as drysalters.

He apparently had political aspirations, for in 1717 he was returned to Parliament as member for Marlborough, but owing to some error about his election, the Committee that was appointed to enquire into the matter discovered, that he had not received a single vote and he was therefore unseated.

Owing to some further political trouble in which he became involved, he fled to France, and there first began to make the pills and drops for which he afterwards became famous.

Through the intervention of his friend John Page, who was a member of Parliament, he obtained a pardon from George II and returned to London in 1733, where he started his career as a quack-doctor.

By constantly advertising the wonderful cures performed with his nostrums, he soon became the talk of the Town.

His introduction to the King, which set the seal on his success according to Dr. Henning, came about in the following manner.

" George II being afflicted with a violent pain of the thumb which baffled the skill of the faculty, sent for the noted Dr. Joshua Ward; who having ascertained the nature of the complaint before he was admitted, provided himself with a suitable nostrum which he concealed in the hollow of his hand. On being introduced, he requested permission to examine the affected part and gave it so sudden a wrench, that the King cursed him and kicked his shins. Ward bore this very patiently and when the King was cool, respectfully asked him to move his thumb, which he did easily and found the pain gone."

The delighted King asked Ward if he could do anything for him, to which the quack replied, that the pleasure of serving his Majesty was adequate reward for him, but he would be grateful if the King would do something for his nephew. The result was, the nephew was made an ensign in the Guards and Ward was presented with a carriage and pair of horses, together with the privilege of driving it through St. James's Park. He further received a vote of thanks from the House of Commons, and protection from interference in his practise from the College of Physicians.

The qualified medical practitioners were naturally much incensed at such favours being accorded to a quack, but nothing transpired to interfere with Ward's prosperity.

The grateful Monarch next provided him with a room in his almonry at Whitehall for treatment of the poor, besides which, Ward bought three houses in Pimlico which he turned into a hospital, where he treated the sick with his remedies with the assistance of several ladies of quality.

Among his patients were the Lord Chief Baron Reynolds, Lord Chesterfield, Gibbon and Fielding, while Horace Walpole also sounded his fame. According to a report in the *Daily Advertiser* on June 10th 1736, " By the Queen's appointment, Joshua Ward Esq., attended at Kensington Palace with eight or ten persons, who in extraordinary cases had received great benefit by taking his remedies. Her Majesty was accompanied by three surgeons and several persons of quality, the patients were examined, money was distributed to them and Mr. Ward was congratulated on his success."

It is said, that Queen Caroline once asked General Churchill, if it was true that Ward's medicines had made a man mad ?

" Yes, Madam," was the General's reply, " and his name was Mead," alluding to the famous Dr. Mead, the King's Physician.

Pope refers to Ward in the lines :

" Of late, without the least pretence to skill,
    Ward's grown a famed physician by a pill."

His remedies were numerous, the principal ones being the pills, which were composed of antimony and dragon's blood, while the drops consisted of a small quantity of antimony dissolved in Malaga wine. Besides these, he made a " White Drop " which consisted of an ammoniated solution of mercury, and two " sweating powders " composed of ipecacuanha and opium, with the addition of hellebore or liquorice. He also had a "Paste", a "Dropsy purging powder" and an "Essence for headache." Two of these at least were effective and useful preparations, for they afterwards became incorporated in the London Pharmacopœia. The " Paste " which consisted of elecampane, fennel and black pepper, became officially recognised as the confection of black pepper, and his " Headache essence " was the original of the compound camphor liniment.

It was the latter application, he afterwards told Mr. Page, that he used to King George's thumb.

Ward who was popularly known as " Spot Ward," on account of a birthmark on one side of his face, bequeathed his book of secret formulæ to his friend Mr. Page, who afterwards published it. A depôt for selling the medicines was established, the profits from which were to be divided between an Orphan Asylum and a Magdalen Institution.

Ward died in 1761, but was not buried in Westminster Abbey in front of the altar, as he expressly desired, according to his will.

An explanation of the marvellous and sudden cures he witnessed by a celebrated quack behind the Royal Exchange, relates a writer of the XVIIIth century, was due to the discovery, that numbers of poor people came up from the remotest parts of the country whose ailments had been pronounced incurable in several hospitals.

" A surgeon assured me, that these wretches I had seen were by way of decoy ducks, hired alternately to attend there and near the Horse guards, twice a week and half-a-crown a week, to pretend to be cured of such diseases as they were instructed to personify ; and that the better-dressed people who came in coaches, and were shown occasionally as private patients upstairs, were hired at a crown each, exclusive of the coach."

CHAPTER XIX

A GENTLEMAN who made it his business to investigate the practises of some of the female quacks in London in the early part of the XVIIIth century, has left an account of his experience, which is not without interest. Let us follow him in his visits. He first called on Madam S—— formerly of Moorfields, " the most frightful Piece that ever eyes beheld in the shape of an old woman, having more antiquity in her face than all Italy and Greece can pretend to show, the crow's feet have taken hold of her cheeks, and wrinkly-age supplies the place of former charms. Her eyes are so far sunk in their sockets, that they look like a pair of dice in the bottom of two red boxes. She is as toothless as a lamprey, yet she knows how to put the bite upon you for all that. She abounds with pomatums and sweet waters, all little enough to qualify the poisonous whiffs about her, which would otherwise out-stink ten thousand pole-cats. She cannot chuse but kiss well, for her lips are perpetually bath'd in oyl and grease, and one would think, that not a drop of water had been laid upon her since the parson sprinkled her at the font.

" We have many other ladies that far excel this old

mumsimus, being as they tell us, not only students in Physick, but in the noble science of astrology.

"Mrs. M—— whom it seems some envious people reported to be dead, acquaints the world that she is still living and where she did in Ayres-street Pickadilly. She'll cast your water and calculate your nativity. Her rattlesnakes, crocodiles and squirrels, will fill you with strange ideas of learning ; her velvet scarf, gold watch and diamond rings will convince you of her great skill in the art of gulling.

"Add to these Susanna K—leus, original daughter, not an imperfect copy, as she calls herself, of Dr. K—leus in Fetter-lane and some hundred more of such female students up and down the Town many of whom have the confidence to put out bills.

"On Southwark side, is a wonderful old fellow who might have been Bucephalus by the size of his head. The hair on his face is sufficient to stuff a couple of cushions, and there is room enough in his beard for birds to build nests. He walks about the streets with a bag of medicines as big as a tinker's budget, and rather than turn a customer away, he will exchange a dose of physick for a consideration of meat and drink. After him is the great Dutchman, Mynheer van Dunder, well-known by his blew coat and red whiskers, all over the town. By the help of his fellow labourer, Jack Pudding, he first gathers a mob, then harangues them in the usual quack language. Then he shows a number of bottles and boxes and shouts, ' Here be de fat of de wild cock, and here be de grease of de dead man, dis be good for dat, and dat for d'other.' "

Addison, who gives his experience of quack-doctors' bills in the *Tatler* in 1710, observes, "If a man has pains in his head, colics in his bowels, or spots in his cloathes, he may meet with proper cures and remedies. If a man would recover a wife, or a horse that is stolen or strayed, if he wants new sermons, electuaries, asse's milk or anything else either for his body or his mind, this is the place to look for them.

"About twenty years ago, it was impossible to walk the streets without having an advertisement thrust into your hand of a doctor, who had arrived at the knowledge of the Green and Red Dragon, and had discovered the female fern seed.

"Nobody ever knew what this meant, but the Green and Red Dragon amused the people, that the doctor lived very comfortably upon them.

"About the same time, there was pasted a very hard word upon every corner of the streets; TETRACHY-MAGOGON, which drew great shoals of spectators about it who read the bill that it introduced with unspeakable curiosity, and when they were sick, would have nobody but this learned man for their physician.

"I once received an advertisement, of one who had studied 30 years by candle light for the good of his countrymen. He might have studied twice as long by daylight and never have been taken notice of.

"There are some who have gained themselves great reputation for physic by their birth, as the 'Seventh son of a seventh son,' and others by not being born at all, as the 'unborn doctor,' who I hear has lately gone the way of his patients.

" Kirleus, the ' unborn doctor,' did a brisk trade in consideration of his being ' unborn.'

" There were two male and two female quacks of the name of Kirleus ; Thomas the father and his son John, Susannah the widow of Thomas, and Mary the relic of John.

"One woman rested her reputation on being the daughter of a ' seventh daughter,' but it is said she was foreclosed in her business and blasted in her fame by a younger twin-sister, who claimed and carried the preference, on the score of her being actually the ' seventh ' in the second order of ' sevens.'

" The walls of the Coffee-houses were hung round with gilt frames containing the bills of ' Golden Elixirs,' ' Popular Pills,' ' Beautifying Waters,' ' Drops and Lozenges,' all as infallible as the Pope. The ' Rainbow ' in particular, I should have taken for a Quacks Hall or the parlour of some eminent mountebank.

" I have seen the whole front of a mountebank's stage, from one end to the other faced with patents, certificates, medals and great seals, by which the several princes of Europe, have testified their particular respect and esteem for the Doctor. I believe I have seen twenty mountebanks that have given physic to the Czar of Muscovy. The Great Duke of Tuscany escapes no better. The Elector of Brandenburg was likewise a very good patient.

" As physicians are apt to deal in poetry, apothecaries endeavour to recommend themselves by oratory, and are therefore without controversy, the most eloquent persons in the whole British nation.

" As for myself, the only physic which has brought me safe to almost the age of man, and which I prescribe to all my friends, is ABSTINENCE.

" In short, my Recipe is ' Take nothing.' "

Among the female quacks who flourished in the XVIIIth century, the most notorious and certainly the most successful, was Joanna Stephens. There is probably no more astonishing proof of human credulity in the annals of quackery, than is instanced in the historic coup of this ignorant and vulgar woman, who succeeded in inducing the British Parliament to pay her the sum of five thousand pounds, for the secret of her quack remedy for the Stone.

The story of this fraud, now almost forgotten, is worth recounting. She began her operations about 1736, by advertising that she had discovered a sovereign remedy for calculus. She was sufficiently cunning to ingratiate herself with a number of aristocratic and influential persons including peers, duchesses and bishops, and prevailed on them to testify, to the wonderful cures she was supposed to have effected by her remedy, and even to allow her to use their names to further her ends.

After enriching herself for some years by the large fees she induced her dupes to pay, and probably anticipating that her popularity would soon be on the wane, she advertised that she was willing to disclose the secret of her nostrums, for the sum of five thousands pounds.

This announcement appeared in the *Gentlemen's Magazine* for April 1738.

" Mrs. Stephens has proposed to make her medicine

publick on Consideration of £5,000 to be raised by con-
tribution, and lodged with Mr. Drummond, banker;
he has received since the eleventh of this month about
£500 on that account."

The newspapers and journals of the time were at once
besieged with letters appealing to the charitable and
benevolent, not to allow such an opportunity of acquiring this blessing to humanity to pass.

The list of subscribers increased daily, and in it appeared the names of the Bishop of Oxford 10 guineas,
the Bishop of Gloucester 10 guineas, the Earl of Pembroke £50, Countess Deloraine 5 guineas, the Earl of
Godolphin £100, the Duchess of Gordon 5 guineas,
Viscount Lonsdale £52 10s., the Duke of Rutland £50,
Lord Cardogan 2 guineas, Lord Cornwallis £20, Earl of
Clarendon £25, Lord Lymington £5, the Duke of Leeds
£21, Lord Galloway £30, the Duke of Richmond £30,
together with many others.

These names are mentioned to show the distinguished
dupes the wily Joanna had drawn into her net.

In spite of all appeals however, the amount subscribed
did not reach more than £1,356, which was not enough
to tempt Joanna to part with her secret.

Her next move was to get her influential friends to
apply to Parliament to grant the full amount she de-
manded, and strange to state, their request to the
Government was successful. A Commission was duly
appointed to inquire into the cures performed by Joanna
Stephens, and the result of their labours is embodied in
the following award, which deserves to be handed down
to posterity as evidence of a Nation's gullibility.

" We, whose names are underwritten, being the major part of the justices appointed by an Act of Parliament entitled : ' An Act for providing a reward to Joanna Stephens upon proper discovery to be made by her, for the use of the publick, of the medicines prepared by her ' . . . do testify, that the said Joanna Stephens, did with all convenient speed after the passing of the said Act, make a discovery to our satisfaction, for the use of the publick of the said medicines and of her method of preparing the same, and that we have examined the said medicines and of her method of preparing the same, and are convinced by experiment, of the utility, efficacy, and dissolving power thereof.

" Jo. Cant, G. Hardwicke, P. Wilmington, C. P. S. Godolphin, Dorset, Montague, Pembroke, Baltimore, Cornbury, M. Gloucester, Tho. Oxford, Ste. Poyntz, Stephen Hales, Jo. Gardener, Sim Burton, Peter Shaw, D. Hartley, W. Cheselden, C. Hawkins, S. Sharp."

How such men as Cheselden and Hawkins were so deceived, it is difficult to comprehend.

And so Joanna, after extracting all she could from her wealthy supporters, succeeded in making the British nation the biggest dupe of all, and pocketed £5000 from the public funds.

The great secret was revealed and published in the *London Gazette* on June 19th 1739 and was as follows :

" A full discovery of the medicines given by me Joanna Stephens, and a particular account of my method of preparing and giving the same.

The medicines are a Powder, a Decoction and
Pills.

The Powder consists of Egg-shells and Snails—both
calcined—

The Decoction is made by boiling some herbs (together
with a ball, which consists of soap, swine's cresses burnt
to blackness and honey) in water.

The Pills consist of Snails calcined, wild carrot seeds,
burdock seeds, ashen keys, hips and hawes—all burnt
to blackness—Alicant soap and honey."

The manner in which these ingredients were to be
prepared follows and need not be recapitulated. It is
sufficient to state that the dose was a drachm of the
powder three times a day, mixed in Cyder or other
liquor, to be followed by half a pint of the decoction.
If the decoction disagreed, the pills were to be sub-
stituted.

This is what the country got in return for its money.
Surely no greater piece of effrontery is recorded in
history.

The success of Joanna Stephens, naturally brought
forth hosts of imitators who also professed to have
discovered similar cures for the Stone.

Sir Robert Walpole became a victim to the soap
treatment, and took a course, consisting of one ounce
of alicant soap, in three parts of lime-water daily. He
continued this treatment for several years and at the
time of his death it was calculated, that he had consumed at least 180 pounds weight of soap, and 1200
gallons of lime-water. After his death, a necropsy was

made by Sergeant-Surgeon Ranby and Cæsar Hawkins, who found three stones in his bladder !

Horace Walpole referring to instances of distinguished persons who fell victims to quackery, says, " Sir Robert was killed by a lithontriptic medicine, Lord Bolingbroke by a man who pretended to cure him of a cancer in his face, and Winnington was physicked and bled to death by a quack in a few days for a slight rheumatism."

CHAPTER XX

THREE GREAT QUACKS

CONTEMPORARY with Joanna Stephens was
Mrs. Mapp, or "Crazy Sally" as she was
popularly called, who was a highly successful bone-
setter. Bone-setting in this country, was for centuries
regarded more on a level with farriery than part of the
surgical art. In some districts it was commonly believed, that it could be transmitted from father to son,
on the presumption, that one having acquired the
"knack," he could communicate it to the other and so
impart the secret of his manipulative skill.

Sarah Wallin was the daughter of a bone-setter, who
lived at Hindon in Wiltshire. Her sister is said to have
been the original of the famous Polly Peacham who
afterwards married the Duke of Bolton.

Crazy Sally, as she came to be called, soon tired of
village life and leaving home, she wandered for a time up
and down the country. She eventually settled at Epsom,
where she practised her art and so gulled the people
of that district in the belief of her powers as a bone-
setter, that they raised a subscription to keep her among
them. Here she flourished, and her fame extending to
London many journeyed down from town to see 'Crazy
Sally.' Her strength was so great, she is said to have been

300 THE QUACKS OF OLD LONDON

able to reduce a dislocated shoulder without assistance. In 1736, she resolved to get married and espoused one Hill Mapp, who was footman to a mercer in Ludgate Hill. The ceremony took place on August 17th of that year, but differences soon broke out between the couple, and the husband ran off a week after the wedding, taking with him a hundred guineas belonging to Sally and some of her portable property. She appears to have been glad to have got rid of him at the price, and did not grieve long over her loss.

Once a week she drove to London in her chariot drawn by four horses, accompanied by outriders and footmen in splendid liveries. It was on one of these journeys, when passing through Old Kent Road she was mistaken by the onlookers for a distinguished but unpopular lady of quality from Germany.

A crowd gathered round the carriage with menacing gestures, but Sally rising to the occasion, let down the windows and thrusting out her head shouted, " Damn your bloods. Don't you know me ? I'm Mrs. Mapp the bone-setter ! " This so amused the mob that they cheered her lustily and allowed her to proceed on her way.

When in London, she made her headquarters at the Grecian Coffee-house, where she operated on her patients. In the *Gentlemen's Magazine* October 1736, some surprising cures are related, which she is said to have performed before Sir Hans Sloane at the Grecian Coffee-house where she came twice a week from Epsom. One of these was " a man of Wardour Street, whose back had been broken nine years and stuck out two inches. A niece of Sir Hans Sloane who was in like condition, was cured, also a gentleman who went with one shoe heel six inches high, having been lame twenty years of his hip and knee, whom she set straight and brought his leg down even with the other."

Sally Mapp, although she was enormously fat and ugly, became the talk of the Town. One account states, " the cures of the woman bone-setter of Epsom are too many to be enumerated ; her bandages are extraordinary neat and her dexterity in reducing dislocations and setting fractured bones wonderful. The lame come to her daily and she gets a great deal of money, persons of quality who attend her operations, making her presents."

Hogarth introduced her into his print " The Undertaker's Arms or Consultation of Physicians," where she is placed between two other notorious quacks of the time, already referred to viz., Taylor and Ward.

Poets sang her praises and ballads were written in her honour. The following lines were published in 1736.

> " Let these, O Mapp, thou wonder of the age !
> With dubious arts endeavour to engage ;
> While you, irregularly strict to rules,
> Teach dull collegiate pedants they are fools
> By merit, the sure path to fame pursue—
> For all who see thy art must own it true."

Her practise so increased, that later on she removed to London and took up her abode in Pall Mall. She attended the first night of the " Husband's Relief " at the playhouse in Lincoln's Inn Fields, when the following ballad was sung in her praise.

" You surgeons of London, who puzzle your pates,
To ride in your coaches, and purchase estates,
Give over for shame, for pride has a fall,
And the Doctress of Epsom has out-done you all,
                                        Derry down.
" In physic, as well as in fashions, we find,
The newest has always its run with mankind ;
Forgot is the bustle ! 'bout Taylor and Ward,
And Mapp's all the cry, and her Fame's on record.
                                        Derry down.
" Dame Nature has given a doctor's degree—
She gets all the patients, and pockets the fee ;
So if you don't instantly prove her a cheat,
She'll loll in her carriage, whilst you walk the
    street.
                                        Derry down."

Sally Mapp gave a plate of ten guineas to be competed for at Epsom and went to see the race run. Curiously enough, the first heat was won by a mare called " Mrs. Mapp," and she was so delighted, that she gave the jockey a guinea and promised to make it a hundred, if he won the plate, but unfortunately for him he lost.

In the end, she took to drinking heavily and is said to have been rarely sober. Patients and friends alike began to fail her, thus she sank into poverty and died in miserable lodgings near the Seven Dials.

Percival Pott a famous surgeon of the time commenting on Sarah Mapp says : " Even the absurdities and imprac-

tibility of her own promises and engagements, were by
no means equal to the expectations and credulity of
those who ran after her, that is, of all ranks and degrees
of people from the lowest labourer up to those of the
most exalted rank and station, several of whom not
only did not hesitate to believe implicitly, the most
extravagant assertions of this ignorant, illiberal, drunken,
female savage, but even solicited her company or at
least seemed to enjoy her society."

The following account of the "Three Great Quacks,"
Mapp, Taylor and Ward, satirising the foibles of the
age is contained in an epistle "To a young student
at Cambridge, written by a friend in Town."

"Whilst you dear Harry, sweat and toil at College,
  T'acquire that out-of-fashion Thing call'd Know-
      ledge.
  Your time you vainly mis-employ, my Friend
  And use not proper means to gain your end,
  If you resolve Physician to commence,
  Despise all learning, banish common sense;
  Hippocrates and Galen never follow,
  Nor worthy Aesculapius or Apollo;
  But to bright Impudence oblations pay,
  She's now the goddess, bears resistless sway,
  Instinct by her, vile Ign'rance gains applause,
  And baffles Physick, Churchmen and the Laws.
  By her such quacks as Ward have cur'd and slain,
  How! Cur'd you cry. Yes, daring Ignorance
  Can cure, as well as kill by perfect chance,
  As fools by prating, such have often hit

Upon a Thought, and blunder'd into wit ;
So Drugs, that learned Mead would not endure,
Dispensed by Ward incautellous may cure ;
From dangerous Revulsions now and then
May save one wretch, and next day poison Ten ;
That one in ten, perhaps may be enough
To raise a name and furnish out a Puff.
And when a quack or thief gets once in vogue,
There still are Idiots to caress the Rogue,
Nay in this wise, polite and well-bred Nation,
Some Fops will poison take to be in fashion.

Come up to Town then Harry, leave the schools,
Your gilded coach shall be upheld by fools,
Come up a novice, get a House and Chariot,
Chuse this, or learnedly to starve in garret,
Pall Mall be thy abode or Grov'nor Square,
An ample crop of fools you'll harvest there.
Here then be ready, with thy nostrum new,
Ting'd like the charlatans, with Red or Blue.
The composition may be any stuff,
Hire people to be cur'd who have no ills,
Then swear 'twas done by thy new Persian Pills,
With care and cost brought o'er from Ispahan,
The only Physick of Great Kouli-Kan.

But this, you say's against the plainest sense,
The more is due to glorious Impudence,
Here in Pall Mall, her rising Honours grow,
Her country seat's not far—at Pimlico ;
Observe the crowd still press about the door,

The Great, the Rich, the Wretched and the Poor.
Hither the Mob with Coronets and Crutches,
Eager alike the Cinder-wench and Dutchess.
Garters and Rags, from Palace and from Stall
Advance, the Mighty, Vulgar and the Small!
Taylor and Mapp too here her reign exalt,
And to her footstool lead the Blind and Halt.
Taylor with learning, wise as any Grandam,
Brushes away and ventures all at Random.
With Lady's hand and playthings bright and keen,
Can cataracts remove and drop serene.
Values no threats nor popular reproach.
Tho' once he'scaped so hard in Dover coach.*

Madam performs her work by pulling, hawling,
And graces all with cursing and with bawling,
The apparatus made with oaths and din,
The Bones pulled sometimes out and sometimes in.
Ladies their lap-dogs, some their monkeys bring,
Each dislocated part ty'd up in sling,
Courted by all, by all admir'd these quacks,
Keep equipages, laugh at dirty hacks,
Here Harry, view the Arts to get a name,
'Tis chance and Impudence must raise your fame,
Assisted by a Paper kept in fee,
That shall displace the News to puff for thee.
What blear-eyed Beggar last he took in hand
And how Mapp made a limping footman stand,
  But if through spleen the learn'd on t'other side,

*Taylor was once mobbed at Canterbury when travelling on the Dover coach.

Your nostrums and your packets should deride,
Hire Bravos to way-lay them in the street
And all who will not like your physick beat.
Or bring from Westminster an Information.
So purge and beat and sue and cheat the Nation.

In this bright Age, three wonder-workers rise,
Whose operations puzzle all the wise,
To lame and blind, by dint of manual slight,
Mapp gives the use of limbs and Taylor sight,
But great Ward, not only lame and blind
Relieves, but all diseases of mankind.
By one sole Remedy removes, as sure
As Death by arsenic, all disease can cure."

Foote, in a satire on the quack and his bills says,
" Jaundice proceeds from many myriads of little flies of
a yellow colour which fly about the system. Now to
cure this, I make the patient take a certain quantity
of the ova or eggs of spiders. These eggs when taken
into the stomach, by the warmth of that organ, vivify
and being vivified, of course they immediately proceed
to catch the flies ; thus the disease is cured, and I
then send the patient down to the seaside to wash all
the cobwebs out of his system."

There were several amusing skits on the speeches of
quack-doctors published in the Georgian era and one
of the best has been preserved.

" Gentlemen,
" I am the famed Paracelsus of this age by name
Seignior Doloso Effrontero, native of Arabia Deserta,

natural son of the wonderworking Chimist-Doctor lately deceased at the Devil's Peak in Silesia, and famous throughout Europe, Asia, Afrique and America, who in pitty to his own dear self and languishing mortals has by the earnest prayers and solicitations of divers Princes, Lords and other honourable personages, been prevailed with to oblige the world with this notice, that all persons, young or old, deaf or lame, blind or dumb, may know whither to repair for present cure in all Cephalalgiers, Paralytical paroxismes, Odontalgias, Apoplexices, Peripneumonias, Empyemias, Palpitations of the Pericardium, Syncopes, Nanseties, arising either from Plethory or a Cacochymy, Disenterias, Iliacal passions, the Scurvies Exanthemata, the Hog-pox, the Henpox, the Small-pox, or the Devil's-pox, the scaldheads, warts, corns, and all other diseases, griefs, wounds, fractures, dolors, pains, and distempers of Nature.

" My medicines are the Quintessence of Pharmapeutical Energy and the cures I have done are above the Art of the whole world.

" Imprimis. I have a wonderful universal, unheard of, neverfailing Hypnotical, Cordiacal, Cephalical, Hepatical, Anodynous, Odoriferous, Renorative, Styptical, Corroborating Balsam of Balsams (made of dead men's fat, rosin and goosegrease) that infallibly restores lost maidenheads, raises demolished noses, and by its abstersive, cosmetick quality, preserves superanimated bawds from wrinkles.

" I have the true Catharmapophora of Hermes Trismegistus, an incomparspagyrical tincture of the Moon's Hornes. I have the Pantimagogon of the Triple Kingdom, that works seven several ways and is seven years in preparing, being last exactly compleated secundum artem by Fermentation, Putrification, Distillation, Rectification, Cohobation, Circulation, Calimation, Sublimation, Solution, Precipitation, Coagulation, Filtration, and Quidlibetification both in Balneo Marie, the Crucible and the Fixatory, the Athanor, the Cucurbite and the Reverboratory.

"A drachm of it is worth a bushel of March dust and if any person happen to have his brains beat out or his head chopt off, two drops seasonably applied, shall recall the fleeting spirits, re-enthrone the deposed Archeus, cement the discontinuity of the parts and in six minutes, restore the lifeless trunk to its pristine vigour.

"I have also an excellent Antipudengragrian Specifick, the choicest Jewel amongst Venus's Regalia, which perfectly cures the Modish disease. I have it under the hands and seals of the greatest Caliphs and Moguls in Christendome. To verificate the reality of my operations—I cured Prester John's God-mother of a stupendous dolour about the Os Sacrum, so that the good lady feared the perdition of her Hucklebone. I did it to the great admiration of that Court, by fomenting her with the Mummy of Nature otherwise called Pilgrim Salve, and the Spirit of Mugwort, Terragraphocated through a Limbeck of Chrystalline transfluences.

"I cured the Duchess of Promolpho of the cramp in her tongue, an Alderman of Grand Cairo, that had lain seven years sick of the Plague, I cured him in two and forty minutes, from whence I was sent for by the Sultan of Gilgal, Despot of Bosnia, who being violently afflicted with spasms, came 600 leagues to meet me in a Go-cart. I gave him such speedy acquittance with his dolour, that next night he danced a Saraband with Flip-flaps and Sommersets, and for my reward presented me with a Persian Horse, a Turkisk Scymitor and 300 Hungarian ducats. I restored virility and the comfort of generation to 150 Eunuchs in the Grand Seigniors Seraglio, and by a pair of my Prolifick Pills, lately caused a virtuous widow that had all her time been barren, to bring forth a lusty boy without the help of a husband, when she was entered the twelfth Luster of her age.

" In a word, the cures I have done are no less innumerable than incredible, for I willingly undertake none but desperate mortal diseases, and love to signalise my practice by performing impossibilities, and therefore if any have occasion to make use of me and render themselves immortal, let them hasten to our habitation.

" Down with your Dust !

" For I am just now sent for, by an extraordinary Courrier to the Mighty Empress of Bomfeze upon important occasions nearly concerning her Royal person.

" Be not sick, too late.

" No money, no cure.

" Gentlemen, That all may know where to repair to me, I live at the Sign of the *Golden Ball* in Fop-alley, next door to the *Flying Hedgehog* where I devote myself wholly to serve the publick, so that when you find me not there, you will be sure not to find me here."

" I made it my business," says an inquirer into quackery and quack-medicines about the middle of the XVIIIth century, " to get the best intelligence I could of the authors of these medicines, as well as of the medicines themselves. I found some of them were professed quacks or sorry chymists, both alike ignorant in the practice of physick. Others simple tradesmen and foolish but bold women. Others again, from some family receipt many years together handed down as some sacred relic, by way of tradition for many ages, till at length falling to the share of one unwilling the mighty treasure should be longer concealed, the same is exposed with some hard name and a large catalogue of its admirable virtues. Thus for the diseases of the head and brain, we have Cephalick Tinctures and Head Pills of divers kinds, Apoplectick Spirits, Balsams and Vapour Drops. For the eyes we have salves and waters without number, not forgetting the good oyster-woman's most excellent ointment, revealed to her husband's great-grandfather in a dream.

" For the gout, we have a Coal-heaver's Decoction, an Old Woman's Plaister and Ointment, a Tarpaulin's East-India Oil, besides the Atyla of a Quacking Surgeon and twenty of the same goodness, good for nothing except to cheat men some of their money and others of their lives.

" We have Consumptions of all sorts pluck'd up by the roots, we have the King's Evil cur'd by that eminent Physico-chyrurgical Parson and you have Mother B—t's Drink for the dropsy and jaundice ; she good woman used to open the pews at St. Sepulchre's when she could spare time from visiting her patients."

CHAPTER XXI

QUACKS OF COVENT GARDEN AND PICCADILLY

A WELL-known figure among the quacks of London in the XVIII century was Colonel Dalmahoy, who sold his nostrums in Water Lane close to the Apothecaries Hall.

He had specifics for every ill, as well as face-washes, love-philtres and charms. He was famous for a wonderful wig he affected, which attracted general attention whenever he took a walk down Ludgate Hill, and was celebrated in a ballad that was sung in the streets at the time. It began :

> " If you would see a noble wig,
>   And in that wig a man look big,
>   To Ludgate Hill repair, my joy,
>   And Gaze on Col'nel Dalmahoy."

Another poet thus commemorates him :

> " Dalmahoy sold infusions and lotions,
>   Decoctions and Gargles and pills,
>   Electuaries, powders and potions,
>   Spermaceti, salts, scammony, squills.
>
> Horse-aloes, burnt alum, agaric,
>   Balm, benzoin, blood-stone and dill,
>   Castor, camphor, and acid tartaric,
>   With ' specifics ' for every ill.

> But with all his ' specifics ' in store,
> Death on Dalmahoy one day did pop ;
> And although he had doctors a score,
> Made Dalmahoy shut up his shop."

Another quack who frequented the neighbourhood of St. Paul's was " Dr." Rock.   The story is told, that one day when sitting in a Coffee-house on Ludgate Hill he heard a man close by express surprise, that a certain physician of great ability had but little practice, while such a fellow as Rock was making a fortune.

" Oh ! " said the quack, addressing the speaker, " I am Rock, and I shall be pleased to explain the matter to you."

" How many wise men think you, are among the multitude that pass along this street ? "

" About one out of twenty," was the reply.

" Well then," said Rock, " the nineteen come to me when they are sick, and the physician is welcome to the twentieth."

In the latter part of the XVIIIth century, Covent Garden became a happy hunting ground for the quacks, and prominent among those who frequented it was a German Jew known as Dr. Bossy. Every Thursday his stage was erected opposite the north-west colonnade from which he would address the crowd.

The platform was about six feet from the ground, open in front, to which access was obtained by means of a broad step-ladder. On one side a table was placed, upon which stood his medicine chest, surgical instruments and other apparatus. In the centre of the stage was a chair, and before seating the first patient in it and commencing his operations, Bossy doffing his gold-laced cocked hat, would advance to the front and bow right and left, to the people who had collected round about.

A very old woman would then be helped up the ladder by his assistants and placed in the chair, after which Bossy would thus begin.

" Dis poor voman vot is . . . How old vosh you ? "

" I be almost eighty Sir. Seventy nine come last Lady Day."

" Ah dat is an incurable disease."

" O dear, O dear, say not so Sir—Incurable ! Why you have restored my sight. I can hear again and I can walk without my crutches."

" No, no, good vomans, old age is vot is incurable, but by the blessing of Gote, I vill cure you of Vot is ilshe. Dis poora voman vos lame and deaf and almost blind. How many hosipetals have you been in ? "

" Three Sir, St. Thomas's, St. Bartholomew's, and St. George's."

" Vot, and you have found no reliefs ? Vot, none— not at alls ? "

" No, none at all, Sir."

" And how many professioners have attended you ? "

" Some twenty or thirty, Sir."

" O mine Gote ! Three sick hosipetals and thirty doctors ! I should vonder vot you have not enough to kill you twenty times.

" Dis poora voman has become mine patient. Dr. Bossy gain all patients bronounced incurables ; pote wid de blessing of Brovidence, I shall make short work of it and set you upon your legs again.

" Goode peoples, dis poora voman vos deaf as toor nails (Bossy holds up a great watch to her ear)

" Can you hear dat ? "

" Yes, Sir."

" O den be thankful to Gote. Can you valk round dis chair ? "

" Yes, Sir."

" Sit down again goode vomans. Can you see ? "

" Pretty so, so, Doctor."

" Vot can you see, goode vomans ? "

" I can see the baker there " (pointing to a mutton-pie man with his board on his head)

" And vot else can you see goode voman's ? "

" The poll-parrot there " (pointing to a parrot hanging in a cage outside Richardson's Hotel)

" Lying old——" screamed back the parrot.

At this the crowd would shout with laughter.

Bossy would wait until the noise subsided, then looking across and shaking his head at the bird, with his hand on his breast would solemnly say, " 'Tis no lie, you silly pird, 'tis all true as de gospel."

Richardson's grey parrot was as well known in Covent Garden as Bossy, and was much addicted to lurid language which she picked up from the basket-women who frequented the market.

The following story of this remarkable bird is related by the elder Edwin : " One day, the nail on which the cage was hung on the front of the house suddenly gave way, and poor Polly, cage and all, crashed down on the pavement. People ran to the spot expecting to find the bird dead, and so apparently it was, but in a few moments suddenly rising and stretching her wings she cried, ' Broke my head by——', and immediately after climbed up the side of the cage with a shriek of mirth."

A fashionable quack who used to travel the continent in great style was an Italian called Mantacinni. A young plausible and loquacious person, he always dressed in the latest fashion and attended by a lackey in gold-braided livery, rode in a splendid chariot drawn by a fine pair of horses. Arriving once at Lyons he boldly announced to the public, that he was able and ready to *revive the dead at will*. He further declared, that in fifteen days, he would go to the common graveyard, and bring to life all who had been buried there for the preceding ten years. This statement naturally aroused great excitement in the city, and he was so mobbed by the people in the streets, that he applied to the magistrates to put him under guard, so that he could not leave the town until he had fulfilled his promise.

This proposition had the effect he expected, which was to inspire confidence, and his door was thronged daily by people anxious to consult him, and to buy his celebrated "Baume de Vie" which he declared to be unrivalled for prolonging life.

As the day approached on which the great event was to take place, the faithful lackey began to get nervous about his master, and feared the result.

" You know nothing of mankind," said the quack to his servant, " Be quiet and wait."

Shortly afterwards, a letter arrived addressed to Dr. Mantacinni which read as follows :

" Sir,
The great operation which you are going to perform has broken my rest. I have a wife buried for some time who was *a fury* and I am unhappy enough without her resurrection. For Heaven's sake do not make the experiment. I will give you 50 louis to keep your secret to yourself."

Soon afterwards, two young men called and besought Mantacinni not on any account to raise their old father, who had been the greatest miser in the city, or they would be reduced to poverty.

They were followed by a young widow who was about to be married. She threw herself at the feet of the quack, and with sobs and sighs, implored him not to bring her late husband back to life.

This kind of thing went on and Mantacinni chuckled as the fees flowed in, but as the day approached the citizens became so agitated, that the chief magistrate intervened and sent for the quack.

" I have not the least doubt," he said to Mantacinni, " that you will be able to accomplish the resurrection in the grave-yard the day after to-morrow, but I pray you to observe, that our city is in the utmost excitement and confusion, and to consider the dreadful revolution the success of your experiment must produce in every family. I entreat you therefore, not to attempt it but go away, so that tranquillity can be restored to our city.

" In justice however to your rare and divine talents, I shall give you an attestation in due form under our seal, that you *can revive the dead* and that it was *our fault* we were not eye-witnesses of your powers."

Mantacinni, concealing his satisfaction, at once consented to the proposal, the certificate was duly prepared and signed, and he left Lyons exultant, his pockets well-lined with the gold of his dupes.

Among the eccentric quacks who were prominent during the latter part of the XVIIIth century was Katterfelto, who used to travel about the country in a large caravan accompanied by a number of black cats. He first sought notoriety by advertising a remedy for influenza, which in 1782 was very prevalent in the country. After reaping a golden harvest he settled in London, and combined the sale of " Dr. Bato's medicines " with a quashi-scientific exhibition, which he opened at 22 Piccadilly.

He was a clever and astute advertiser, as may be judged from the following, which appeared in the *Morning Post*, on July 22nd 1782.

" Mr. Katterfelto has in his travels had the honour to exhibit with great applause before the Empress of Russia, the Queen of Hungary, the Kings of Prussia, Sweden, Denmark and Poland ; and since his arrival, in London he has been honoured with some of the Royal Family, many Foreign Ministers and Noblemen, and a great many Ladies of the first rank.

WONDERS ! WONDERS ! WONDERS ! WONDERS ! Are now to be seen by the help of the Sun and his new invented Solar Microscope, and such wonderful and astonishing sights of the Creation, was never seen before in this or any other kingdom, and may never be seen again.

" The admittance to see these wonderful works of Providence is only, Front seats 3s., Second seats 2s., Back seats 1s. only from 8 o'clock in the morning till 6 in the afternoon, at 22 Piccadilly, this day and every day this week.

" Mr. Katterfelto has likewise, by a very long study, discovered at last, such a variety of wonderful experiments in natural and experimental philosophy and mathematics, as will surprise all the world.

" The apparatus he has received only but a few days, and are not to be equalled in Europe, can be seen every day with his greatly admired and new improved Solar Microscope.

" The insects on the hedges will be seen larger than ever, and those insects which caused the *late influenza* will be seen *as large as birds*, and in a drop of water the size of a pins head, there will be seen above 50,000 *insects;* the same in beer, milk, vinegar, flour, blood, cheese, etc., and there will be seen many surprising insects in different vegetables, and above 200 other dead objects.

" N.B. After his evening lecture, he will discover all the various arts on dice, cards, billiards and E.O. tables.

" Mr. Katterfelto likewise makes and sells ' Dr. Bato's medicines ' at 5s. a bottle, which has cured many thousand persons of the late Influenza."

A later advertisement reads as follows :
" Dr. Wall of Oxford will be very glad if his friends

in town will meet him at Mr. Katterfelto's Exhibition Room at 22 Piccadilly at 12 o'clock."

On March 7th 1783 he announced in the *Morning Post* :

" At Katterfelto's Exhibition Room, last Wednesday, between 12 and 1 o'clock, a Gentleman dropt a white purse with three guineas in gold and a note of hand for £2,000, payable to Captain Paterson, after the 26th of March, from G.H. at Cavendish Square. If the gentleman who dropt the above purse will call personally on Mr. Katterfelto, and give a further description of that purse and note of hand, which is payable to him, he will be very glad to return the same to the gentleman.

" Mr. Katterfelto will, this and every day till the 22nd of March next, from 10 in the morning till 5 in the afternoon, shew his Occult Secrets and his new improved Solar Microscope, if the Sun appears ; which has surprised the King and the whole Royal Family. And Mr. Katterfelto as a Divine and Moral Philosopher, begs leave to say, that all persons on Earth live in darkness, if they are able to see, but will not see his wonderful Exhibition."

" After his Lecture this evening, he *will surprise the Company beyond description*."

In his last advertisement he announces that :

" The King of Prussia has given orders, that 100,000 men of his best troops, are to hold themselves in readiness to march at 24 hours notice, and if so, we are to expect that the noted philosopher Mr. Katterfelto, as he belongs to the Death's Head Hussars, will be obliged to depart from England sooner than he expected.   Before he goes abroad, he is to exhibit once more before the Royal family."

Whether Katterfelto marched off with the Death's Head Hussars accompanied by his black cats, is not recorded, but that is the last we hear of him.

CHAPTER XXII

A QUACK'S EMBALMED WIFE

ABOUT 1770, there might have been seen riding in the Row on a fine morning, a weird-looking little man with a long grey beard, armed with a large white bone and mounted on a white pony painted with purple spots. His name was Martin van Butchell, who after a small beginning as a quack-doctor, blossomed out as a *Super* dentist in a large house in the upper part of Mount Street, Mayfair.

He was an expert advertiser and his eccentricities brought him into further notoriety. In the *St. James's Chronicle*, May 18th, 1776, he announces, that he makes " Real or Artificial Teeth from one to an entire set, with superlative gold pivots or springs ; also gums, sockets and palate formed, fitted, finished and fixed without drawing stumps or causing pain.

"The Nobility and Gentry sending a guinea with written notice are assured of Mr. van Butchell's punctual attendance, if the fee is taken at his house in the upper part of Mount Street, Grosvenor Square, who (keeping strict honour and profound secrecy) neither goes journies nor gives credit, but aims and is acknowledged to excel in performing the various operations with instruments peculiarly his own, invented through a series of close applications, extensive study and much experience.

" Mr. van Butchell having made all his employers happy (though many had been hurt by dentists esteemed famous) hopes discerning, generous minds, when others cannot please will apply to him. VAN BUTCHELL IN WHITE MARBLE IS ON THE DOOR."

" On March 23rd 1769 a noble Earl graciously wrote, dated and subscribed four weighty lines, to declare the ability and uprightness of Mr. van Butchell, which those in doubt may see."

On the death of his wife in January 1775, he had her body embalmed. This was carried out by Dr. William Hunter and Mr. Cruickshank, the surgeon, by injecting the vascular system with oil of turpentine and camphorated spirit of wine and packing camphor into the cavity of the abdomen.

Arrayed in a garment of fine linen and lace, the body was then placed in a case with a glass lid, covered with a curtain, and was kept thus by van Butchell in his sitting room. He usually introduced the embalmed wife to his visitors as his " dear departed."

On this becoming known, his house for a time was besieged by curious people who wished to be introduced to the " preserved lady," until van Butchell was at length obliged to issue the following notice, which appeared in the St. James's Chronicle, Oct. 21st, 1775.

" Van Butchell (not willing to be unpleasantly circumstanced, and wishing to convince some good minds they have been misinformed) acquaints the Curious, no stranger can see his embalmed Wife, unless (by a Friend personally) introduced to himself, anyday between Nine and One, Sundays excepted."

The following epitaph was written on the preserved lady, who was never buried, and whose remains are now in the Museum of the Royal College of Surgeons.

" Here unentombed van Butchell's consort lies,
  To feed her husband's grief or charm his eyes,
  Taintless and pure her body still remains,
  And all its former elegance retains,
  Long had disease been preying on her charms,
  Till slow she shrank in death's expecting arms,
  When Hunter's skill in spite of Nature's laws,
  Her beauties rescued from corruptions jaws ;
  Bade the pale roses of her cheeks revive
  And her shrunk features seem again to live.
  Hunter who first conceived the happy thought,
  And here at length to full perfection brought.
  O lucky husband ! blest of Heaven,
  To thou the privilege is given,
  A much-loved wife at home to keep,
  Caress, touch, talk to, even sleep
  Close by her side, whene'er you will,
  As quiet as if living still
  And strange to tell, that fairer she,
  And sweeter than alive should be ;
  Fair plump and juicy as before
  And full as tractable, or more.
  Thrice happy mortal ! Envied lot,
  What a rich treasure hast thou got ;

Who to a woman can lay claim,
Whose temper's every day the same."

According to a contemporary account, Hunter was successful in injecting a carmine fluid into the blood-vessels of the body which give it a life-like appearance. Thus the lips and cheeks retained their colour, and glass eyes were inserted which added to the effect.

For some years, van Butchell enjoyed a period of domestic tranquillity which he had never previously experienced, but in spite of this happy state of affairs and his declared fidelity to his ' dear departed,' he again became smitten with the charms of another fair lady and married her. The new Mrs. van Butchell was not long in raising a very natural objection to having the body of her predecessor in her sitting room, which ended in the removal of the embalmed remains of the first wife to another place, and so peace was again restored.

A quaint walking stick which belonged to van Butchell, bearing a silver band offering five shillings reward to the finder, is still preserved in the Museum of the Royal College of Surgeons.

Another curious character, but a man of considerable ability, was John Hill who was born about 1761. After beginning life as an apprentice to an apothecary, he eventually pushed his way to a prominent position in the fashionable world of his time.

Quack and charlatan though he was, he had undoubted literary talent, and wrote a work on botany which extends to twenty-six folio volumes and contains 16,000 plates. He was also the author of several books on history and romance, and wrote a number of plays and poems.

Garrick alludes to his work as a playwright in the following lines :

> " For physic and farces, his equal there scarce is—
> His farce is his physic, his physic a farce is."

He is said to have had an intolerable temper and became obsessed with the idea that everyone was his enemy.

Finding his literary efforts unremunerative, he started a journal called *The Inspector*, in which he advertised his medicines, and once a week contributed to it a " lay sermon."

The journal met with success and growing wealthy through the sale of his herbal remedies, he took a town house in St. James's Street and a country residence at Bayswater, between which he travelled in a smart carriage and pair.

Once thus established, he made several influential acquaintances and married a sister of Lord Ranelagh. He is said to have been a frequent guest of the Duchess of Northumberland and a friend of the Earl of Bute.

His remedies chiefly consisted of tinctures, prepared from certain herbs such as sage, valerian, and water-dock, which he declared were infallible panaceas for all diseases.

A wit once sent Hill these lines :

> " Thou essence of dock, valerian and sage,
> At once the disgrace and the pest of this age.
> The worst that we wish thee, for all of thy crimes,
> Is to take thy own physic and read thy own rhymes."

To this Hill replied :

" I'll take neither sage, dock, nor balsam of honey,
    Do you take the physic and I'll take the money."

John Hill died of gout in 1775, a disease he had
professed to cure by means of his tincture of dock, and
his end is thus referred to in a ballad of the time.

" Poor Dr. Hill is dead ! Good lack !
    Of what disorder ? An Attack
    Of Gout. Indeed ! I thought that he
    Had found a wondrous remedy ;
    Why, so he had and when he tried
    He found it true—the Doctor died ! "

CHAPTER XXIII

BRODUM, SOLOMON AND GRAHAM

A T a period when several medical men of eminence were not above selling their own remedies, the composition of which they kept secret, it is not to be wondered that they had imitators among practitioners of another kind.

Sir Hans Sloane sold an eye salve and his name was associated with a " Milk Chocolate," while the famous Sir Richard Mead made a secret powder for the bite of a mad dog.

Others did not scruple about using quack remedies, as in the case of the celebrated surgeon Sir Charles Blicke, to whom Dr. Abernethy served his apprenticeship. He is said to have favoured an application called "Plunket's Caustic" in cases of cancer, which is said to have been composed of white oxide of arsenic, and sulphur, mixed with some innocuous herbs.

Richard Guy is said to have purchased the secret recipe for its preparation, which was published in *Lloyd's Evening Post* about 1754.

It consisted of " Crowsfoot, Dog Fennel, Crude Brimstone of each 3 middling thimblefuls and white arsenic the same quantity. Beat well and mix in a mortar, and make into small balls the size of nutmegs, and dry in the sun."

A quack who attracted the attention of the College of Physicians but who eventually got the best of the encounter, was Dr. Brodum, a German Jew, who is said to have begun life as footman to Dr. Bossy, the mountebank of Covent Garden.

He started business by selling two nostrums, one of which he called his "Nervous Cordial" and the other "Botanical Syrup."

He first lived in Albion Street, Blackfriars Road, and put a plate inscribed "Dr. Brodum" on his door like a regular practitioner, but afterwards removed to a large house in a fashionable square in the West-end.

One of his pamphlets, advertising his remedies, is dedicated to the King, and is entitled, "A Guide to Old Age or a cure for the Indiscretions of Youth." In this he states, "the efficacy and virtues of Brodum's medicines are supported by a cloud of witnesses," and offers magnanimously, "to wait upon any lady or gentleman for a fee of five guineas a week."

On the attention of the College of Physicians being called to his operations, he was summoned to appear before the President and Censors to explain his mode of practice. Brodum appeared, and when questioned as to his knowledge, declared that he was only acquainted with Hebrew and English. He explained that he did not attend patients at their residences, and prescribed only his own medicines, for which he had obtained the Royal patent.

The President observed that they did not want to

interfere with the sale of his medicines, but he must stop using the title of doctor on his door-plate and must not take fees.

Brodum however declared, that he had a medical diploma from the Marischall College of Aberdeen, and was entitled to style himself doctor. When asked when and how he got it, he replied, he paid for it like others did, and his certificate had been signed by a Fellow of their own College. He refused to remove his brass-plate from the door and so the matter ended.

Contemporary with Brodum was another Jewish quack called Dr. Solomon who originally hailed from Liverpool. His great nostrum was the " Cordial Balm of Gold," which he declared contained " no other mineral but Gold, ' Pure virgin gold ' and the ' true Balm of Mecca.' "

According to a book he wrote called " the Guide to Health" which he dedicated to the Earl of Mansfield, his Balm was "the real pure essence of gold, together with some of the choicest balsams and strengtheners in the whole materia medica. The process is long and laborious and not a single drop can be produced under nine weeks digestion, and the elements of which it is composed are only obtained with still greater labour, being extracted from the *seed of gold*, which our alchemists and philosophers have so long sought after in vain."

The preparation which he called " Anti-Impetignes or Balm of Gold," is said to have been nothing more mysterious than brandy, while his " Cordial Balm of Gilead " consisted of rosemary, sage, mace and turpentine, flavoured with lemon.

Solomon was a well-known figure in the streets and

when taking his daily promenade, always carried an imposing gold-headed cane in his hand.

In 1805, Solomon built himself a fine house in a suburb of Liverpool surrounded by a large garden and shrubberies, where he lived in great style and kept a coach, which he drove with a fine team of horses.

When Madame Tussaud was forming her original collection of wax works, she asked Solomon's permission to add his effigy with other celebrities. The quack was greatly flattered and invited Madame to visit " Gilead House " to carry out the operation of making the mask.

Solomon was directed to lie on his back, while Madame proceeded to mould the wax to his features. Either through nervousness or forgetfulness, she forgot to leave any air-holes over the mouth and nose. The unfortunate victim bore the agonies of suffocation for some time, until he found it unbearable, and jumping up tore off the mask and flung it across the room, exclaiming, " By Heaven, Madame, do you wish to stifle me ? "

By no persuasion however, could Madame Tussaud induce him to let her repeat the operation.

Solomon was fond of entertaining his friends and some of his patients to dinner, and the story is told that on one occasion, a local wag wishing to draw him, after the wine had gone round, suggested that he should give his guests something more delicious than anything that had yet been offered to them.

" Anything I have in my house is at your disposal," replied the genial host.

"Then dear Doctor, let us taste your 'Balm of Gilead.'"

Solomon at once ordered his servant to bring each guest a bottle of the famous Balm. These were uncorked, and on tasting the liquid, the company pronounced it more palatable than any of the wines previously offered to them. The evening passed and the guests rose to depart. At a signal from the "doctor," the servant again appeared bearing on a silver salver a number of small envelopes, which he passed round to each person. On opening them, they found they each contained a bill for two guineas, the price per bottle of the Balm they had recently consumed and so much appreciated.

On their remonstrating with their host, Solomon replied with a bow,

"Gentlemen, I invited you here as my guests. The Balm is my business, you must therefore each pay me two guineas."

Whether he got paid or not, is unrecorded.

A story is also told of one of his lady patients whose husband discovered that she was constantly consulting the quack and consuming bottle after bottle of his "Balm of Gold." She had conceived such a liking for the nostrum that he could not get her to cease taking it. Finding that many of her friends had acquired the same habit, he took counsel with their husbands and together they concocted a plot to take their revenge on Solomon.

On a certain dark night they despatched a messenger to his house, asking him to come at once to see a sick patient who lived a little way out in the country, and he was to be sure to bring with him several bottles of his celebrated Balm.

The quack set out on foot along the country lanes towards the patient's house and at a very lonely part of the road, he was suddenly pounced upon by four men enveloped in cow hides who had been hiding behind a hedge. With long horns and tails they looked like devils incarnate and frightened the unfortunate Solomon out of his wits. He sank on his knees and begged for mercy, but his tormentors seized him and dragged him into a field close by. After making him swallow the contents of the bottles of his nostrum that he had brought with him, they ducked him in a pond and finished by tossing him in a blanket.

The plot was successful in so far that Solomon incensed at the outrage (the story of which had spread abroad) left the town and for a time settled in Birmingham. He died in Liverpool and was buried according to his wish in the front garden of his house.

A popular ballad of the time referring to the two quacks ran :

" Brodum or Solomon with physic,
    Like death, despatch the wretch that's sick,
    Pursue a sure and thriving trade ;
    Though patients die, the doctors paid !
    Licensed to kill, he gains a palace,
    For what another mounts a gallows."

"While Solomon flies on the wings of the wind,
    His magical Balm of Mount Gilead to find,

Little Brodum stands stewing his herbs in a copper,
And to vend his decoction for gold he thinks proper.
                                    Derry down."

A brief allusion here must be made to James Graham
called the " Emperor of Quacks " who became notorious in London about 1780, and was one of the most
extraordinary charlatans of his day.*

Born in Edinburgh, where he obtained some medical
training, after travelling in America and practising as an
oculist in Bath, he established himself in a fine house in
the Royal Terrace, Adelphi. It was known as the
" Temple of Health " and there he gave advice and
sold his nostrums, which included an " Electrical
Aether " " Nervous Aetherial," " Elixir of Life," and
his " Imperial Pills."

The " Temple of Health," which was lavishly decor-
ated and furnished regardless of expense, owing to his
glowing advertisements soon became a fashionable resort.

On the ground floor was a Central Hall the walls of
which were hung with offerings such as crutches, ear-
trumpets and other appliances left by grateful patients.
In the basement was the laboratory, where the medicines
were prepared and dispensed. In the first room above
was Graham's cabinet, where he sat for consultation,
and close by, the most wonderful place of all, called the
" Great Apollo Apartment " where stood the " Temple
Sacred to Health."

In another room, the chief attraction was the " Grand
Celestial Bed," an extraordinary piece of furniture,

*For a full account of Graham's career and operations see " Mysteries of
History " page 260, by the same author.

by means of which, according to Graham, "Children of the most perfect beauty could be begotten." A fee of five hundred guineas a night was charged to those who wished the privilege of occupying it.

On special occasions, an " Ode set to music was performed in the ' Great Apollo Apartment ' by a selected choir, accompanied by the organ and a band of instrumentalists."

Here also in the evenings, Graham delivered his lectures and displayed his medico-electrical apparatus, which included a " Magnetic Throne " on which patients were seated to receive electrical treatment. Graham charged a fee of a guinea for his first consultation, and five shillings and half-a-crown for admission to his lectures.

For a time the " Temple of Health " became the vogue and was crowded every day by people of fashion, many of whom doubtless came out of curiosity.

It was so successful, that in 1781, Graham took Schomberg House in Pall Mall, and after fitting it up at considerable expense, opened it as the " Temple of Health and of Hymen," where he installed another " Celestial State Bed " of greater magnificence than the one in the Adelphi.

But in spite of his flamboyant advertisements, bills and pamphlets, the new establishment did not prove the success he anticipated ; creditors began to press for payment, and eventually he had to shut it up.

The failure of his Temples caused Graham to seek pastures new, and for a time he left London and travelled the country, lecturing at Liverpool, Newcastle and Edin-

burgh. While in the latter city he offended the authorities through one of his lectures, and was arrested and
thrown into prison until he had paid a fine.

On his return to London, he attempted to found a
new religious sect which he set out in a pamphlet
entitled :

" Proposals for the establishment of a new and true
Christian Church," but this met with little support.
Southey says, that " Graham was half-mad and his
madness at last got the better of his knavery. He would
madden himself with ether, run out into the streets,
and strip himself to clothe the first beggar he met."

There is little doubt in the end his mind became un-
hinged and he died suddenly at the age of 49, in Edinburgh, in the year 1794.

CHAPTER XXIV

THE ARTIST QUACK—THE DANCING-MASTER QUACK

ALTHOUGH the quack-doctor often styled himself an artist, it is rarely we find an artist who turned quack-doctor, as in the case of Philip James Louther-bourgh, a well-known painter of the XVIIIth century. He was born in Germany in 1740 but leaving his native country early in life, he began to study art in Paris and became a pupil of Vanloo and of Causanova.

After travelling in Switzerland and Italy, he came to England in 1771 and was engaged by David Garrick as chief designer of scenery at Drury Lane Theatre, and also assisted him in a reform in theatrical costumes. He was elected a member of the Royal Academy in 1781 and painted many marine and battle pictures of large size. One of his principal works, " Earl Howe's victory on June 1st, 1794 " now hangs in Greenwich Hospital.

In 1783 he settled at Chiswick and there he came under the influence of Richard Brothers and began seriously to study the occult. In the end he became convinced that both he and his wife, were gifted with the power of prophecy and of healing disease without medicine.

As soon as this became known, the Loutherbourgh's house was besieged by crowds of sick and ailing people, in so much he found it necessary to issue tickets to admit the would-be patients to his consulting room. He charged no fee and distributed the tickets gratuitously, until it was discovered that they were being sold outside the house in the crowd to those tired of waiting, for as much as five guineas each.

In a publication of the time it is stated, " that Mr. De Loutherbourgh who lives on Hammersmith Green has received a most glorious power from the Lord Jehovah viz ; the gift of healing all manner of diseases incident to the human body, such as blindness, deafness, lameness, cancers, loss of speech and palsies."

A Miss Mary Pratt, who constituted herself a kind of advertising agent for the Loutherbourghs, published an account of the cures the artist-quack and his wife had performed, from which the following is extracted.

One case was that of Mary Ann Hughes, " whose father is chairman to her Grace the Duchess of Rutland who lives at No. 37 in Ogle Street. She had a most violent fever, fell into her knee, went to Middlesex Hospital, where they made every experiment in order to cure her but in vain ; she came home worse than she went in, her leg contracted and useless. In this deplorable state she waited on Mrs. Loutherbourgh who, with infinite condescension, saw her, administered to her and the second time of waiting on Mrs. Loutherbourgh she was perfectly cured."

Another case was that of Mrs. Hook of Stable Yard, St. James's, who had two daughters born deaf and dumb. She waited on Mrs. Loutherbourgh who looked on them with an eye of benignity and healed them.

" I heard them both speak," remarks Miss Pratt. "Let

me repeat with horror and detestation," she concludes, " the wickedness of those who have procured tickets of admission and sold them for five and two guineas a-piece!—whereas this gift was chiefly intended for the poor. Therefore Mr. Loutherbourgh has retired from the practice into the country (for the present) having suffered all the indignities and contumely that man could suffer, joined to ungrateful behaviour and tumultuous proceedings. I have heard people curse him and threaten his life, instead of returning him thanks, and it is my humble wish that prayers may be put up in all churches for his great gifts to multiply."

The tumultuous proceedings mentioned, no doubt refer to the fact that one day owing to a disappointed patient, Loutherbourgh was severely handled by the crowd outside his house and this happened on several occasions.

He gave asylum to Cagliostro and his wife, when the couple fell on evil days during their last visit to London, and Mrs. Loutherbourgh accompanied Madame Cagliostro to Switzerland when she finally left England to join her husband.

A quack appliance, by means of which the inventor declared, that " disease could be drawn from the human body," first exploited in America and eventually exploded in England, was the so-called " Metallic Tractors."

They were the fore-runners of the many electrical and magnetic appliances of a later period, by means of which the public have been gulled.

The inventor of the "Tractors," Elisha Perkins, was

originally a student of Yale, and afterwards practised medicine at Norwich, Connecticut, in the United States.

About 1795, he conceived the idea that metals had an influence if applied to the body externally, and after carrying out experiments, he perfected an appliance which he called his " Tractors."

They consisted of two rods composed of brass and iron, about three inches long, rounded at one end and pointed at the other. One side of each rod was half round, while the other was flat, and on the latter were stamped the words " Perkins Patent Tractors."

He is said to have made them in a small furnace, concealed in the wall of one of the rooms of his house. According to his own account, one rod was composed of copper, zinc and gold, while the other was of iron mixed with silver and platinum.

They were probably made of brass and iron which cost him about sixpence, but he managed to sell them at five guineas a pair.

Perkins claimed by the use of his Tractors, that the body could be freed from disease without any other treatment. When applied, it was necessary they should always be drawn downwards, and in obstinate cases friction was to be used until the skin became red.

Finding the local medical society sceptical of his claims for the virtues of his tractors, Perkins left Norwich for Philadelphia, where he was received with enthusiasm at the various hospitals and infirmaries he visited to demonstrate his wonderful appliance.

The members of the Congress then in Session, fully believed his story, and George Washington purchased

a pair of the Tractors for his family, and he also found a
patron in the Lord Chief Justice.

Perkins patented the Tractors on February 19th, 1796
and they had a very large sale throughout the United
States, but his old colleagues in Norwich were still
unbelievers, and the Medical Society of Connecticut
eventually passed a resolution that, " Perkins' theories
respecting his tractors were delusive quackery, and
called upon him to appear at their next meeting to
answer for his disgraceful practices." He was shortly
afterwards expelled from the Society.

Finding his popularity beginning to wane in America,
he decided to send his son, Benjamin Douglas, to England
to introduce the Tractors to Britishers. On his arrival,
he established himself in a house in London that was
formerly occupied by John Hunter the famous surgeon,
and began operations by publishing a book dealing with
the scientific aspects of his father's discovery.

About this time, an epidemic of yellow fever broke out
in New York, and Elisha Perkins again came before the
public, with a remedy he declared to be infallible for
that disease. It is said to have consisted of common
salt and vinegar diluted with three parts of hot water,
however, it failed to save the life of the originator of the
remedy, who contracted the disease and died shortly
afterwards.

Meanwhile, Benjamin succeeded in launching the
Metallic Tractors in London and was selling hundreds at
five guineas a pair. They were sent over from America
in parcels each containing two hundred. Many Clergy-
men, including the Chaplain to the Prince of Wales,

Lord Henniker and other influential personages, testified to their wonderful power.

The caricaturists seized on the rage, and Gilray published an amusing drawing of the results of using the " Tractors," which were said to cure a burn or a scald in five minutes. Poets and ballad singers sang their praises, and even Byron, immortalised them in the following lines in his " English Bards and Scotch Reviewers."

> " What varied wonders tempt us as they pass !
> The Cow-pox, *Tractors*, Galvanism, Gas,
> In turns appear to make the vulgar stare,
> Till the swoll'n bubble bursts—and all is air."

They were also thus alluded to in a popular song :

> " Arm'd with twin skewers see Perkins by main force.
> Drag the foul fiend from Christian and from horse."

The Royal Society accepted a pair of the famous appliances and a copy of Perkins' book, while a " Perkins Institute and Dispensary " was established for the poor, with Lord Rivers as president and a committee of other misguided persons.

All was going well, until Dr. John Haygarth, a medical practitioner of Bath, who had strong suspicions of their value, suddenly exposed the fraud.

He shaped a pair of tractors out of two pieces of wood and painted them to appear like the metal appliances, and with these he produced even greater cures than with the originals. Together with a friend, Dr. Falconer, he sent these wooden imitations to other physicians, who

forthwith reported astonishing results, which they published.

The bubble was thus burst and Benjamin Douglas
Perkins packed up his trunks, together with a rich
harvest of some 50,000 dollars which he is said to have
reaped in London, and returned to his native country.

A quack-doctor who combined the callings of a dentist
and dancing-master was Mr. Patence, who carried on his
various activities in Bow Court, Fleet Street, at Ludgate
Hill and the Strand, between 1771-76.

He announces in the *London Gazette*, "that his ingenuity in making artificial teeth and fixing them without the least pain, can be attested by the Nobility, and
he hopes to be honoured by the rest of the great.

"His medicines preventing all infections and sore
throats, have been experienced by several and as for
dancing, he leaves that to the multitudes of the ladies
and gentlemen whom he has taught and desires to be
rewarded no more than his merit deserves, *nor no
less*."

As an instance of his skill as a dentist, he cites the
case of a lady who applied to him with her jaw-bone
broken, by having a tooth extracted by another lady.
She had a sound front tooth in her hand and two others
just ready to drop from their sockets, but he put them all
back again.

Later on, he announces in a bill that, "Patence,
whose works, cures and operations form his supremacy
over every dentist in the Kingdom, also all physicians,
curing man, woman and child, when no one of them can
give relief ; demonstrates by his daily replacing black,

nauseous teeth, with those comprising six different enamels, which are warranted never to turn black.

" He also cures by occult demonstrations, all diseases of the glands and King's hereditary Evil."

In the *Morning Chronicle* of 1776, he boldly announces his discovery, of a marvellous cure-all, which he calls his "Universal Medicine or Supreme Pills, invented by Patence, Dentist and Physician to several of the Royal family." In introducing this arcana, he says, " I shall offer no apology for my medicine, which is well-known to give ease and satisfaction in palsies, gout, rheumatism, piles, fistulas, cancers of any sort, King's Evil, hereditary infections, jaundice, green sickness, St. Anthony's Fire, convulsions, consumptions, scorbutic diseases, pains in the head, brain, temple, arteries, face, nose, mouth, and limbs, for which there is nothing upon the earth surer, softer or better.

" The Universal Medicine also restores lost hearing and sight, renews the vital and animal vitalities, gives complexion to the face, liveliness to the whole structure, and many times has given unexpected relief on the *verge of eternity*."

He concludes by stating, " they require no confinement, eat and drink what you please, and if they do not answer the end proposed, I will return the Money. The real *worth of a box is Ten Guineas* (curiously reminiscent of a well-known pill advertised at the present time) but for the benefit of all, with proper directions, it is sold for three shillings ; with personal advice, ten and sixpence."

As late as 1776, Patence was still flourishing, for in an

announcement he makes in that year which is headed, "To be sold for Five thousand pounds," he states that, "He still has the unspeakable happiness of relieving all who come under his care. His medicine was never gained by book knowledge, nor was it ever known to the faculty, ancient or modern, but acquired by real ingenuity and work.

"To show its safety, sovereignty and efficacy, either when in health or sickness, Mr. Patence constantly *takes his own pills* to preserve his own health, and gives them to children even in the mouth, in all cases."

What greater proof of their virtues could one have than this personal testimonial from the inventor ?

Towards the close of the XVIIIth century, when the old types of quack and mountebank were beginning to pass away, came the development of the quack medicine, which largely owed its popularity and success to the increased facilities for advertising. Whereas in earlier times, the quack had to rely upon his vocal powers and bills to sell his wares, by means of the press, the quack-medicine vendor was able to address thousands.

Even in those days, fortunes were amassed from the sale of quack nostrums such as Godbold's "Vegetable Balsam." The originator of this concoction began life as a ginger-bread baker, and it is stated, that for ten years after launching it, he cleared £10,000 a year from its sale. He had a fine house standing in a park near Godalming in Surrey, which is said to have cost him £30,000. Heath says he "was a sociable, hospitable fellow, but illiterate and vulgar in conversation."

A tablet in Godalming Church perpetuates his memory and is thus inscribed :

" Sacred to the memory of Nathaniel Godbold, the inventor of that admirable medicine for consumptions and asthmas, the Vegetable Balsam, who departed this life, Dec. 17th 1799."

Another quack remedy well-known about the same period and from which the proprietor is said to have made £5,000 a year, was " Velno's Vegetable Syrup." The inventor, whose name was Swainson was originally a woollen draper, and a man of good education, being well acquainted with Greek and Latin. He had a house and grounds at Twickenham, where he made a botanical garden of considerable extent containing many rare plants.

" It is a remarkable fact," says a writer a century ago, " that England which claims to be the centre of civilisation, should contain a population more quack-ridden, more credulous as regards the efficacy of universal secret specifics for the cure of disease, than any other country in the world."

Whether this is true or not to-day, it is extraordinary what an influence the mysterious still has on the human mind. There appears to be in almost every one, a vein of credulity and superstition against which argument is useless. The disposition to be humbugged often preponderates in our nature over reason and common sense. The vast fortunes that have been made from the sale of quack medicines in recent times and the enormous amount spent in advertising them, prove that the same credulity that characterised our ancestors still exists.

The advance of education has made little difference in depriving people of this quality, in fact men of education often fall easier dupes to the quack than those who are ignorant.

A man may be able in politics, in art, in literature, in science or in business, and yet be a believer in quackery of one kind or another. If any one is bold enough to assert that he has a remedy which cures certain diseases and reiterates it often and loudly enough, he is sure to get a following of believers among whom will be found persons of ability and position. This is confirmed again and again in the history of quackery.

One has but to compare the bills of the charlatans and beauty-doctors recounted in the preceding pages, with the advertisements of their modern successors that abound in our daily and weekly papers, to realise, that human vanity and folly have not altered, and that the quacks of to-day vary but little in their methods from the quacks of old London centuries ago.

INDEX

A

B

347

INDEX